OF
ANATOMY

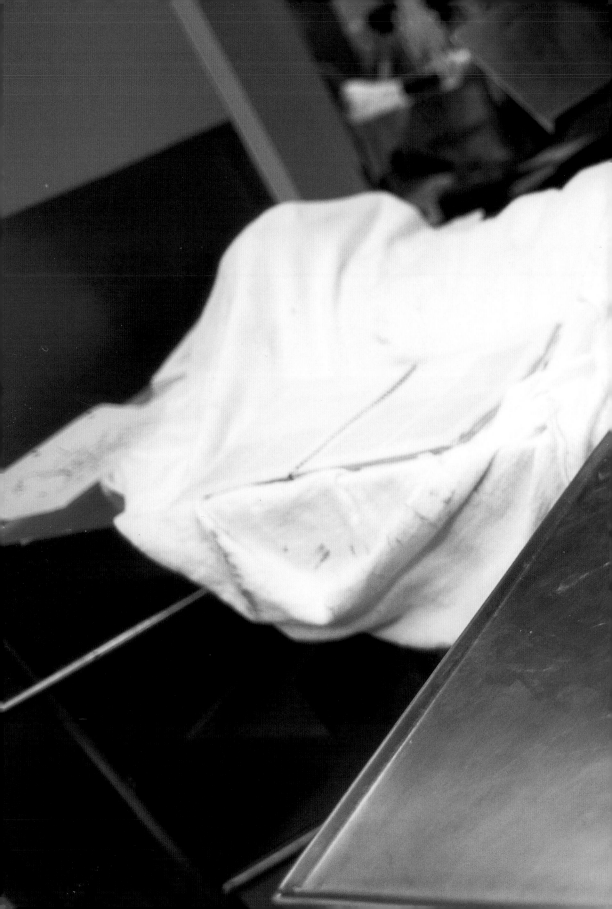

AUTHOR'S NOTE:

Photographs and journal excerpts are presented chronologically
to reflect the order of the documented dissection process.

Photo captions are provided to identify journal writers.

ANATOMY
of
ANATOMY
in images and words

MERYL LEVIN

Foreword by
ABRAHAM VERGHESE, MD

THIRD RAIL PRESS, INC.

FOREWORD

Looking back now, it is difficult for me to pinpoint the moment when I decided to try to get into medical school. My parents were both physicists, and my brothers were whizzes at math, but, alas, I had no head for sums. I loved reading, though. I loved the solidity of words on a page. It was Somerset Maugham's *Of Human Bondage*, which I read when I was very young, that sealed my career choice. Something about Maugham's protagonist, Philip, who failed at art and turned to medicine, made medicine seem to me a passionate pursuit—the equal of art, but even safer. The most diligent artist might find he or she had no talent, but hard work generally meant one could succeed in medicine. And there was little math involved with medicine; it had more to do with words, with, as Maugham wrote, the study of "humanity, there in the rough."

Medical school began for me with the dissection of the upper limb. Other subjects were taught that year, but, strangely, it is only the anatomy experience that lingers. I signed out my big box of bones and carried its rattling contents home to my bedroom. I had my copy of *Gray's Anatomy* as well, a hefty, compact book. The thought that I would have to know every page in it was more than daunting—it seemed humanly impossible. Our first assignment was the brachial plexus, the complex bundle of nerves that emerge from the spinal cord to innervate the upper limb. I memorized that section in *Gray's* before the first class.

On the first day, my partner and I propped the dissection manual against the shoulder of the shriveled woman whose corpse we shared with two others. I felt I could see the brachial plexus in my mind's eye, as if the words I had memorized the previous night were building blocks that stacked themselves up just so. And, over the next few days, as we took scalpel to skin, a magical thing happened: there, one morning, was the brachial plexus, just as I had imagined it, in the depths of the armpit. Admittedly it was not as neat and polished as the figure in the book. Still, there it was, real, vibrant—*alive* in that very dead corpse. As if it had just now rested from years of labor and it took a workman's pride in its muddied appearance, bits of flesh still clinging to it, some of its minor branches frayed and trampled by our inexperienced fingers. What a wonderful affirmation this was of the power and the tangible nature of words! After all, who has ever stripped flesh and seen a theorem? Who has found a differential equation lurking beneath a blood vessel?

Some eight weeks later we finally finished the upper limb, and we took the oral examination that followed. I passed! I topped the class! We went *en masse* to a bar and got quite drunk. I remember I had a sense (quite false, of course) of mastery. In the secular setting of that dimly lit bar, there was no need for such words as we had learned: *pronator teres, flexor carpi radialis,* and my favorite, *opponens digiti minimi.* We were, we felt, an elite group. Unlike the non-medicos in the bar, we could gaze from shoulder down to the delicate curl of the fingers with the knowledge that we knew how it was all held together.

No, the year was not all roses. In fact, the year was hellish, and it is only now under the retrospectoscope that I can color it rosy. My performance in the first oral exam was, as it turns out, my best, and things deteriorated sharply after that. The trouble was that the under-the-hood peek into the inner workings of the body, magical as it felt, was balanced by the need to memorize so much information that we were convinced we would go mad. In our darkest moments, prior to each oral exam, we cursed, we wondered what good any of this did us. Did we really need to know the innervation to the muscle of the big toe, or the structures that came and went through the diaphragm? If we were going to be surgeons, we would surely have to relearn this anyway. How useful was any of this if you were going to be, say, a psychiatrist? Somehow most of us survived that year. And of course, once we were done, we were doubly arrogant, supremely condescending to our juniors who were just starting out, telling them that the torture of that year was entirely justified.

The fine details of anatomy that I used to know have been forgotten, but the big picture is still intact. And islands of memory still remain that, like an *idiot savant* I can call up, dredge up a detail here and there to impress the hell out of the medical students under my tutelage on the wards. Yes, I can still chant out my first mantra: "the brachial plexus is formed by the union of the ventral rami of the lower four cervical nerves and the greater part of the ventral ramus of the first thoracic nerve...." Those words bring it all back: the angst, the sleeplessness, the fear, the intensity of that year of anatomy.

I hark back to that first year often. I am reminded of it in the hospital where it is, of course, of practical use. But I am reminded of it outside the hospital, too. The shape of a skull in an airport lounge invites me to label its parts. A photograph of a tennis player—forearm extended, lunging for a ball, muscles shining through the skin—calls up the brachial plexus and the flexor muscles that radiate out like a pinwheel from the medial epicondyle of the humerus. I obsess some nights about the last few paragraphs of each section in *Gray's*, where it was pointed out in small type, set off from the rest of the text, that there were many variations on the "normal" structure that we had so painfully learned. Some sleepless nights I percuss my body, sounding out air-filled lung and then the dull thump of liver, and then the tympanitic note of air in the belly. Is my heart really on the left side? Could I be one of those whose pancreas divides into two discrete parts, or completely encircles the duodenum? Does my median nerve bifurcate at the head of the radius, or does it divide higher up as it did in the corpse I dissected? Do I have a solitary kidney, or are mine coupled together like Siamese twins? Such lovely, scary obsessions that people who never dissected the body are spared.

I struggle to this day to find words for that seminal year, for the way it marked my transition into this life of a clinician, and the way it has shaped my worldview. Indeed, words alone cannot do it, cannot quite do justice to that year.

And that is why these remarkable photographs, and the accompanying written thoughts of students going through the same rite are so powerful. There it is, in color, in the flesh: The living studying the dead. The dead instructing the living. The shock of nail polish on fingers whose skin has been stripped away to expose the scaffolding. The arteries and nerves and muscles revealed beneath the skin are at once new, and yet timeless, unchanged in their details from when I studied them more than two decades ago. The chain is unbroken.

Oh, and yes: there on a blackboard, and there in the depths of an armpit, and there on a textbook page is the brachial plexus which was my talisman, my siren call, the instrument of my initiation. I cannot help myself, I begin to mumble when I see that, rocking my body as is my wont, reciting these words I can never forget: *the brachial plexus is formed by the union of the ventral rami of the lower four cervical nerves and the greater part of the ventral ramus of the first thoracic nerve...*

Abraham Verghese MD, FRCP(C)
Grover E. Murray Distinguished Professor of Medicine
Texas Tech University

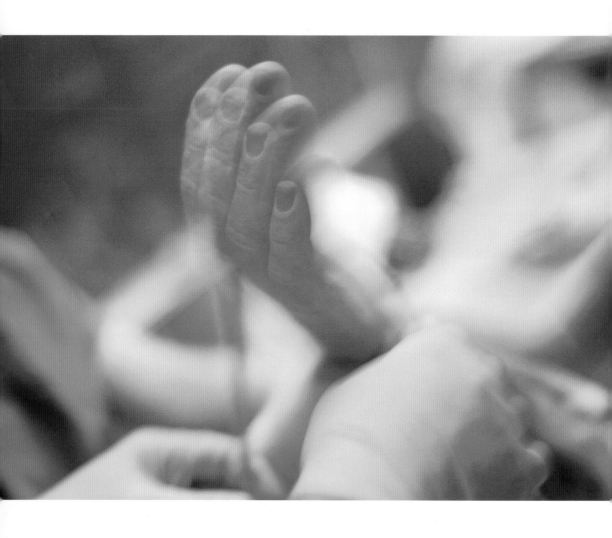

Our professors have made a special point to emphasize what a unique privilege it is to be able to dissect a human cadaver. Not too long ago, doctors had to pay off gravediggers to acquire them. But we are lucky. Contrary to lay belief, our cadavers have not been pulled out of the East River. They were willed by their owners, while they were living, to be used for scientific purposes. I feel a sense of awe for these brave souls.

−Rajiv

It is the day before Gross Anatomy starts.... I've always heard stories about how people faint or vomit when they first see the bodies, but I never thought I would be like that. Now, I suddenly feel very nervous. I am not too worried about the workload; I will have plenty of time to worry about that. I am nervous about the actual dissection. Suddenly the thought of cutting up a dead body scares me to death. I'm not sure if I can handle it.... I can barely sleep in anticipation of the novel experience that awaits me in the morning.

−Tara

By Manhattan standards, this early January morning seems unseasonably warm. As I walk through the front door of the educational building at Cornell University's Medical College, the humid air follows me inside. The building stands on York Avenue in the heart of New York City's hospital district. One floor below street level the air is thicker still, but here it is heavy with anxiety, expectation, and the smell of formaldehyde. For the class of 2001, it is Day One of Gross Anatomy.

The students move quickly from the stairwell to the hallway and into the men's and women's bathrooms. There, they change into surgical scrubs to begin the strange and often transforming ritual performed by so many medical students before them—the dissection of the human cadaver.

Singly and in groups, the students dart out of the changing rooms and move quickly to their pre-assigned dissection tables. Only whispers are audible as all 101 first-year medical students wait for class to begin.

I try to hide my own nervous anticipation at entering this room filled, at first glance, only with death. I place my camera bag down in a corner, hang one camera around my neck and walk around the room, slowly taking my first few pictures. I wonder how I will adjust to this strange, cold space.

Cornell's large anatomy lab is split into quadrants, with four bodies in each area. One side of nearly every cadaver has already been dissected by a Teaching Assistant who will work closely with the group of five or six students assigned to each table. Before today's class, the TAs dissected one side of the chest, and this morning the students will do the other. Later on, the TAs will dissect one arm and the students the other, and so on.

Senior Professor, Dr. John Weber, addresses the students by microphone. After his brief welcome, class commences. This, the first day of the semester, begins with a lesson on the upper chest—its muscles, arteries, veins, and nerves. The TAs speak simultaneously to their respective groups. Their arms motion from chalkboard diagrams, to teaching skeletons, and finally, to their own cadaver dissections on the tables around which the students gather. The room fills with talk of the brachial plexus and the posterial triangle, and with a consuming stench.

—ML

THE ARM 1

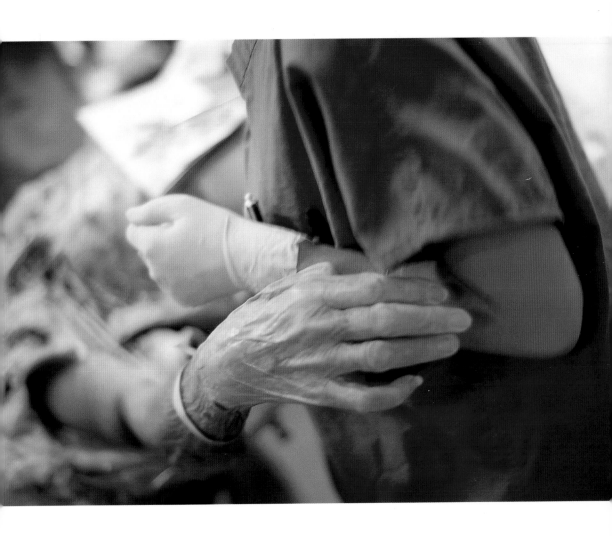

It happened so fast. One minute I was running to class finishing my cup of coffee, and the next minute I'm in front of a chalkboard, watching the teaching assistant explain the subject area to be covered today. No different from any other day—a teacher, a bunch of students gathered around. But lying on the metal table right next to me was a real, live, dead body. Well, not really. But a dead body. I looked around the room at all the other students. They were standing in groups with clipboards clutched to their chests, just like I was. They were surrounding a TA, paying attention to the information being fed to them, and occasionally taking notes. All their faces pointed toward the blackboards.

This amazed me. Were they actually listening? Were they aware of the presence of the bodies beside them? Could they pay attention to what was being taught? I couldn't. The only thing that could keep my attention were the fingernails on the body next to me. I didn't expect the bodies to be wearing fingernail polish, or have well-manicured nails. This elderly body had on opaque, whitish polish with blue hues, a color I couldn't imagine on my own grandmother. It was from the collection of light blues and purples that had pervaded the fashion scene last year, and thus found its way to the fingers of many seventh-grade girls. Here it was on *her* nails, perhaps painted by her granddaughter visiting her in the hospital....

From the minute I laid eyes on my own Anatomy cadaver, I looked for clues that would help me piece together her life. I don't know why that was important to me. I wondered why she decided to donate her body to science, and then I wondered if I could make that same decision. Did she know what was in store for her when she signed the consent form?

As I looked around at all the blades and scissors and other sharp metal utensils strewn around the room, I wondered if I knew what was in store for the both of us.

–Hilary

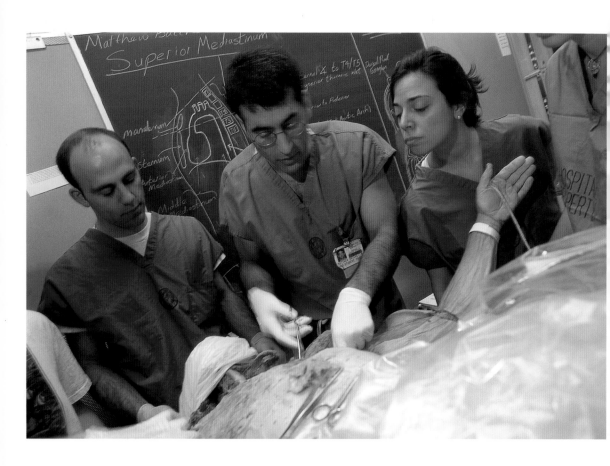

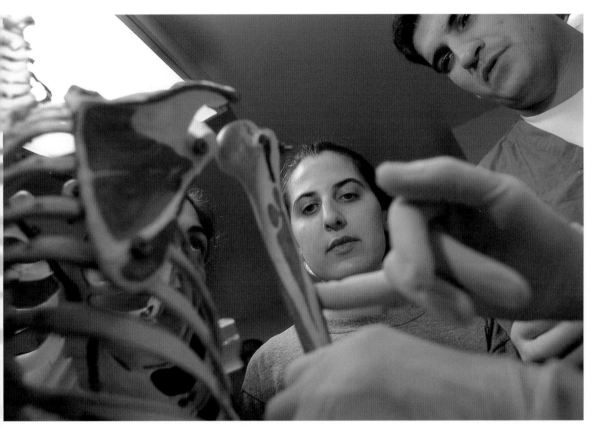

Carrie (center) and classmates learning the structure of the arm.

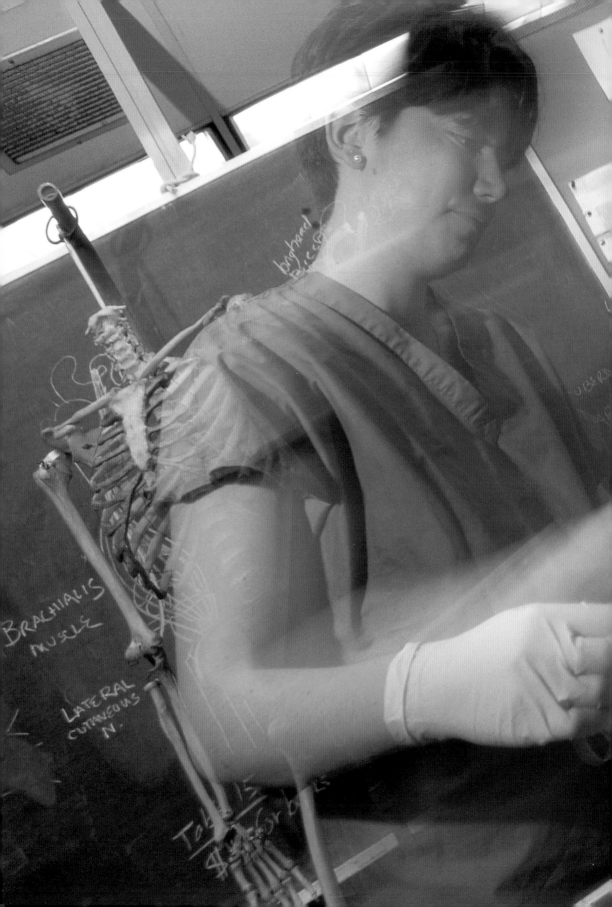

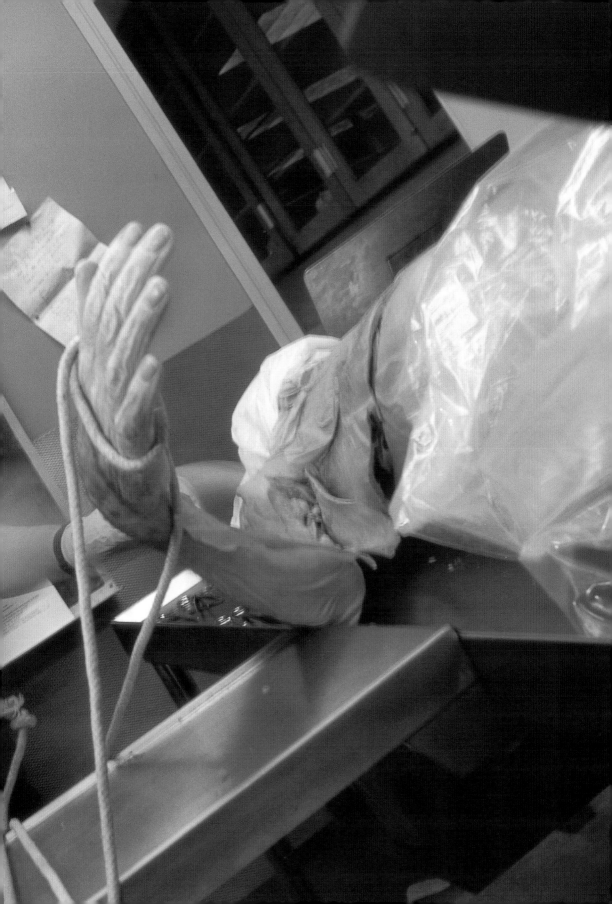

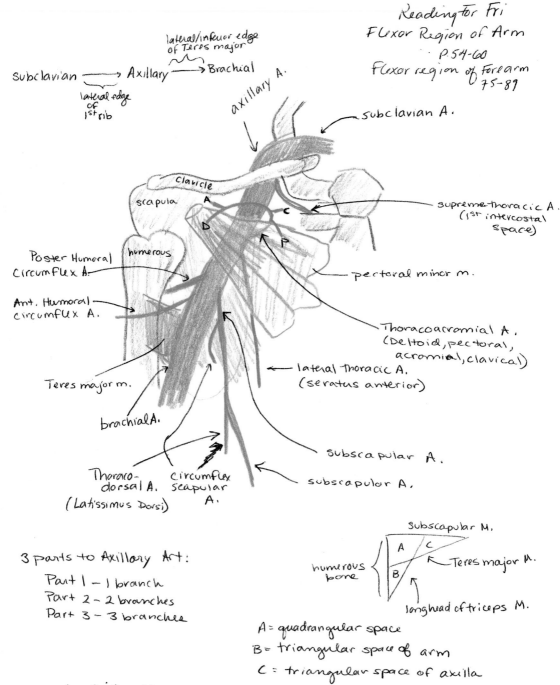

subclavian ——→ Axillary ——→ Brachial

lateral/inferior edge
of Teres major

lateral edge
of
1st rib

axillary A.

subclavian A.

clavicle

scapula

A

C

D

P

supreme thoracic A.
(1st intercostal
space)

Poster Humoral
Circumflex A.

humerous

pectoral minor m.

Ant. Humoral
circumflex A.

Thoracoacromial A.
(Deltoid, pectoral,
acromial, clavical)

Teres major m.

lateral thoracic A.
(serratus anterior)

brachial A.

subscapular A.

Thoraco-
dorsal A.

Circumflex
scapular
A.

subscapular A.

(Latissimus Dorsi)

3 parts to Axillary Art:

Part 1 — 1 branch
Part 2 — 2 branches
Part 3 — 3 branches

Subscapular M.

A   C

humerous
bone

B

Teres major M.

longhead of triceps M.

A = quadrangular space
B = triangular space of arm
C = triangular space of axilla

A = Axillary Nerve
 + Post. Humoral Circumflex A.
B = Radial Nerve + brachi perfunda A.

C. = circumflex scapular A.

After changing into my New York Hospital green scrubs, sporting booties over my shoes, I marched into the lab. The aura was incredible. Seeing the lines of cadavers on top of the tables, the excitement hit me. The ghastly, somewhat emaciated female cadaver was ours.... Once we received instruction on the anatomy of the region to be studied, we began. I was the first to start dissecting at our table. With some dexterity acquired from performing rat [research] surgeries, I cut into her thorax. I felt chills run down my back. The flesh was very tender, with little resistance. This was my first cut, possibly the first step toward a career in surgery.

–Hansoo Michael

■ ■ ■

Despite our having been in classes for five months now, I think I am not the only one who feels that with this initiation, medical school is truly just beginning. The six students in my group (including myself) moved tentatively around the wrapped, covered body. I didn't have a sense of the individuality of this body. He was an older white male, but it was not until I stared at the top of his black chest hair that I thought of his life as a person. In fact, what I thought of was his wife. I don't know why, or even if he was married. But his bankrupt maleness—the hair on his pallid chest on his lifeless body on a metal table in the basement of a building—jarred me.

Throughout this first class, I found my thoughts shifting back and forth, from wondering about the life of my cadaver to the beeper I was wearing attached to my green scrubs, which at any moment could signal my wife's labor with our second child. The life/death cycle that I find myself immersed in could not be more overtly obvious. I feel privileged to be able to experience these bookends of life simultaneously.

The most memorable aspect of my first child's birth was when the OB/GYN called out into the quiet delivery room as my wife and I held our newborn son, "Time of birth: 9:52 am." I thought, "My God, this is when it all begins for him; this is the moment his life starts." It was very powerful.

When we discovered a hospital bracelet with the date of death on the embalmed wrist of our cadaver, I began to wonder about his last moments of life. Was he scared and alone, or at peace and with family? What was he thinking about, if anything, as death overtook him? And what compelled him during his life to want to leave his body to science—the ultimate donation of earthly goods? Had he ever seen an anatomy lab? Did he realize what would become of him? It was then I realized what a gift from him this was—what a privilege it provided us. I think I sensed this feeling from everyone in our group. It's almost as if we had a tacit agreement to do the best job of dissecting we could as a way of thanking and honoring him.

–Michael

We were told that our cadaver would be our first patient. I thought that was an interesting take on the situation. At first glance, my group's cadaver certainly didn't look human. Her skin had a plastic texture, her insides a muddy gray color rather than the brilliant reds and blues I naively expected from looking at the textbook atlases. She looked so small, frail, sexless even. But then I saw a blister on her toe. And on another cadaver, nail polish. So they were human, once. Still? I'm not sure. I wish someone would talk to us and help us to deal with the confusion.

–Carrie

■ ■ ■

Tufts of dark hair streaked with bits of gray peek out from under the small piece of sheet and curl gently on her neck. A little matted with embalming juice, her hair has lost its luster. The embalmers used the side of her neck for their entry site, sewing their work up with coarse thread. The butcher-job made the right posterior triangle a little difficult to reconstruct, particularly for a novice like me.

In all this cutting, the human body seems to have been left behind. In some way, it has to be forgotten in order to allow us to cut and learn without our thoughts being intruded on by an awareness of the enormity of our actions. On the other hand, when the cadaver becomes merely a set of interweaving arteries and nerves, much is lost.

–Rebecca

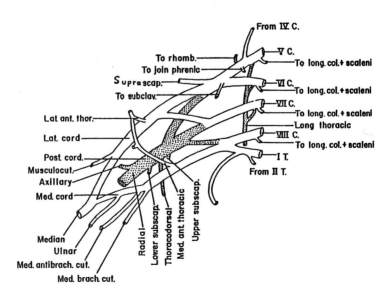

Fig. I

The room was both a morgue and a classroom. At the beginning of Anatomy, whenever I entered the room, I had a hard time separating the idea of a morgue from my mind. The cadavers were not yet classroom learning tools, but only dead bodies. This caused me to view my own body in a different light. In a way, I was repulsed. I looked at my naked body in the shower and thought of hers. Though her aged, lifeless body did not hold a close resemblance to my own, I couldn't help but think that the life-giving blood that coursed through my vessels was transient and would some day stop, and that I would become like her. In the first few days and nights of class, I had many thoughts about the cadaver. She accompanied me to sleep.

Soon, however, and surprisingly fast, the morgue faded into a classroom and the cadavers became our classroom tools. I don't know exactly when it happened, although most of us experienced the transition earlier than we might have expected. I think it may have to do with the amount of material being thrown at us at once, forcing us to focus on what we are here to learn. Every day marks a different part of the body—the forearm, the posterior triangle, the hand, the back. With each day, there are nerve pathways to follow, muscle organizational layers to memorize, arterial supplies to etch into our minds. With each piece of skin removed and dissected, our cadaver's veins and muscles are explored, and she becomes less human, more like a living version of Netter's textbook cartoon drawings. We've begun to appreciate the unique and irreplaceable learning experience offered by studying the body firsthand.

–Hilary

Dr. John Weber (left) teaching the brachial plexus.

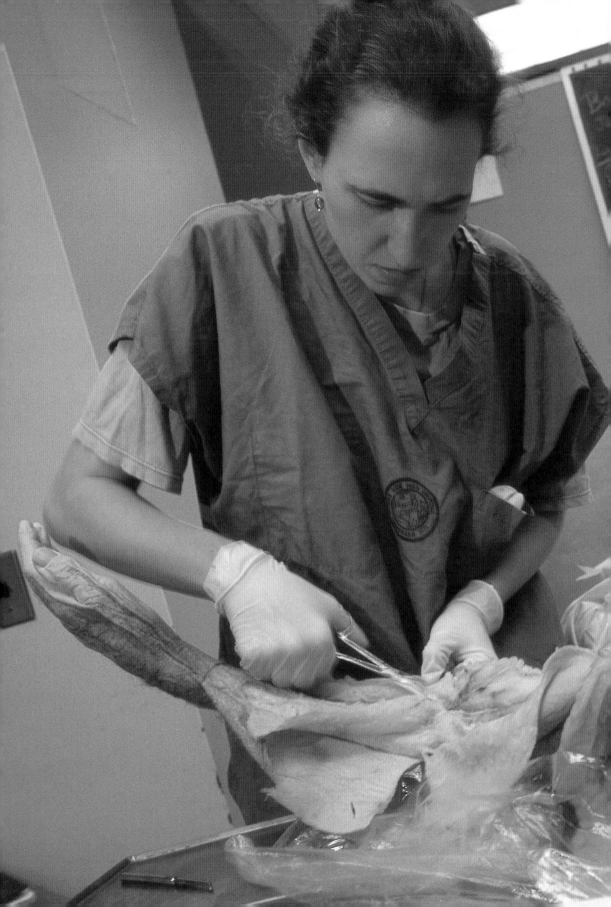

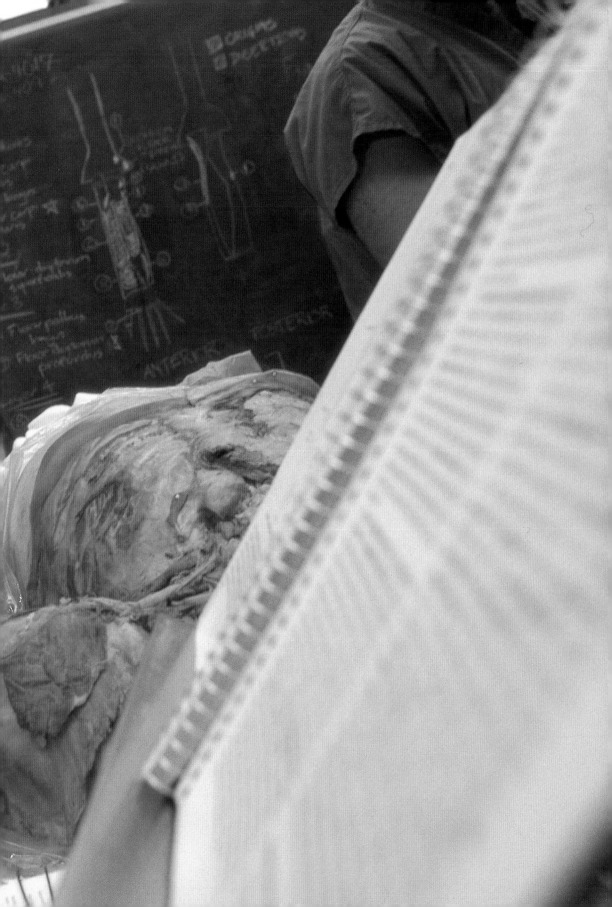

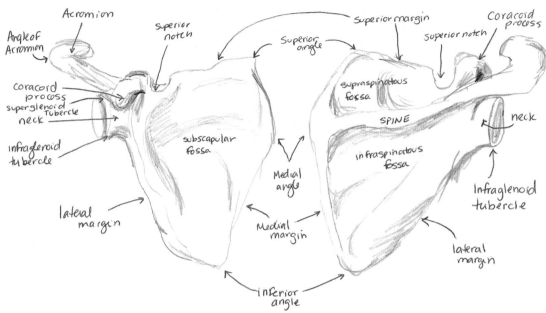

Labels on figure:

Angle of Acromion — Acromion — superior notch — Superior margin — Superior notch — Coracoid process

Superior angle

coracoid process — supraspinatous fossa

supraglenoid Tubercle — SPINE

neck

infraglenoid tubercle — subscapular fossa — infraspinatous fossa — neck

Medial angle — Infraglenoid tubercle

lateral margin — Medial margin — lateral margin

inferior angle

Origins

subscapular fossa = supscapularis

infraglenoid tubercle = long head of triceps

supraglenoid tubercle = long head of biceps

Acromion = deltoid

Coracoid Process = coracobrachialis
+ biceps
(short head)

Superior margin (ventral) = omohyoid

Spine = deltoid muscle

supraspinatous fossa = supraspinatous

infraspinatous fossa = infraspinatous

inferior angle (dorsal) = latisimus dorsi

lateral margin (dorsal) = superiorly = Teres Minor
inferiorly = Teres major

Insertions

medial Margin (dorsal) = levator scapulae
= Rhomboid minor
= Rhomboid major

spine/Acromion = trapezius

medial margin (ventral) = serratus Anterior

coracoid process = pectoralis minor

I have been complaining a lot. Actually, it's more like vocalizing my dislike for Gross Anatomy. I hate it. I really do. I hate it. I hate it.

Phew. It feels good to write that—therapeutic in a way. Emotionally, I've been jumping on and off the biggest, scariest roller coaster of my life. Sometimes I feel confident, excited, professional, and shall I dare to say, smart? Most of the time, though, I feel very small, insignificant, overwhelmed, out-battled, outsmarted, outwitted, and totally and completely out of my league.

I didn't know what to expect from this experience. I tried to prepare. I was not going to be one of those wimps who fainted at the sight (or smell) of a cadaver. I was not going to be scared off by the "hard work" the course promised. I was going to shine. So I talked to my friends at other medical schools and hung on to every word they said. They told me I'd need a "Gross Anatomy bra," a scrunchy [hair tie], and even special socks, because the smell would permeate everything I brought into that lab; that I'd need to shower ten times a day and go back to the lab every night. It was a lot to take in.

I even tried to read about Gross Anatomy. I read a book called *First Cut*, which detailed the anatomy experience at another medical school. I got really nervous from the book and had to stop reading it....

This experience is intense in the emotional and, unfortunately, also in the academic sense. There are days when I don't think I'm going to make it.... I may confidently stab my probe into the cadaver, but inside I am a mess. I am crazy with worry that I won't understand something, can't find a structure, or won't be able to spit back the incredible amount of information we are expected to memorize. I don't know how to create good study habits for this class. I don't know how to make sure I don't stay up all night, every night, like I was in danger of doing this past (first) week.

I think that the academic is interfering with the emotional. I don't have time to think. I am afraid that because of this I have dehumanized my cadaver, probing her lifeless body like a piece of meat (I have become near vegetarian), cutting veins and nerves that "we don't need to know for the test." I am running around to other cadavers in desperate search of an elusive structure. Most people are, I think.

–Carrie

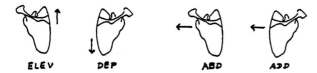

ELEV   DEP   ABD   ADD

Today I said *excuse me* to a dead body. Leaning over to take a closer look at the quadrangular space in the axilla, I bumped into the cadaver's hand stiffly cocked in the air. Without thinking, I excused myself, only to realize seconds later that I was talking to a dead person.

I am surprised that I don't find Anatomy gross or overwhelming. It's actually very interesting. The human body is exceedingly intricate and beautiful. I went in for a couple of hours after class today. There were too many people hovering around the cadaver, so I went to study our CT scans. At first, things were clear and then as I moved down the [CT] plate, things started to move around. Then it all popped out clear again as the 3-D images correlated with what I had seen in the body....

–Rebecca

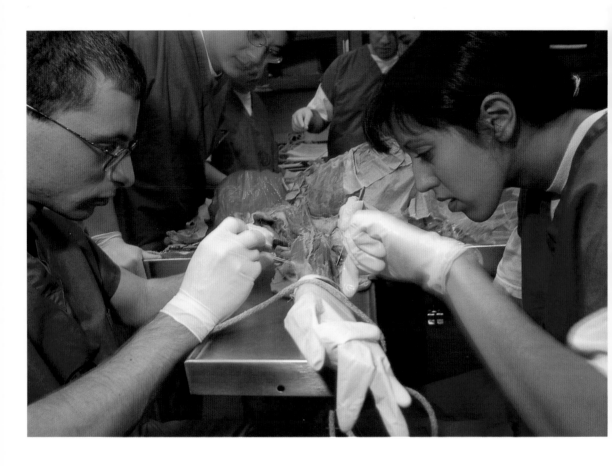

Michael dissecting the hand.

Today we did the hand. Now I am on the crosstown bus back to the West Side, and I can't stop looking at people's hands. I feel like tapping someone on the shoulder and saying, "I know what it looks like inside there—it's beautiful!"

What incredible organization: it's simple and complex at the same time. I strum the back of my seat with my fingers and try to visualize all that is going on inside, like which muscle groups are involved, which nerves, and the order of their electrical commands. I think of my son and how small his hands are and how everything is there functioning, but in miniature. It's miraculous. And then I remember backing into our cadaver's rigid left hand, splayed open, palm-side up at the end of his outstretched yellow arm.

–Michael

A dry, square flap of skin, connected only on one edge, covered the middle of his palm. The dissection incision must have been made with a sharp knife, because I can still trace all the lines of his hand.

He has a deeply imprinted lifeline, a pronounced Mound of Venus, and a long fate line. According to his palm, he must have been a rich man. But I have no way to know if any of this is true. There aren't any designer clothes here, or casually displayed Mercedes keys to announce high status in society. His hair is sticking up because of preservatives, ruining any stylish haircut he may have had. Also gone are any expensive colognes. Now I can only smell the formaldehyde, and the faint odor of decomposing death where the chemical has not been effective.

I continue to search his body for any clues that might show a correlation to the life he led. The tag on his wrist reads "DOD: 12/12." So he died two weeks before Christmas in some unknown year. Gone forever is the softness of his touch, the warmth of his heart, the richness of his experiences.

His uncircumcised penis tells me nothing about his love life. So much for the pronounced Mound of Venus. As for the long fate line, if I took an imprint of his palm and sent it to all the palmists in the world, not one would be able to guess his ultimate fate.

I can't help thinking about his really long education line. Suddenly I realize that at last I have found something that I know is true. I don't know if this man even graduated from high school. But the education he will give me about human anatomy will stay with me forever.

I have finished my dissection of the wrist and hand. It is three in the afternoon, and I have to pick up my daughter from school. I hold her hand tightly as we cross the street. She notices, but doesn't say anything. Her hand is soft and warm despite the January cold. This is what life feels like, I say to myself. I have learned something about the human touch. I will never hold someone's hand the same, old, ignorant way again.

–Rajiv

The hand is a beautiful piece of artwork. So complex and yet amazingly simple. Nothing extraneous—the exact number of muscles, tendons, nerves, and arteries necessary to do the job. I found it exhilarating to cut back the skin of the palm. My dissecting techniques have certainly improved. I managed to cut and peel back the entire skin of the wrist and palm while only nicking one nerve. Is surgery an option?

When we flipped over the cadaver yesterday to do the shoulder and back, we could see that her skull was empty. The top of it had been sawed off by a previous class's neurological dissection. Now, there was just an empty yellow-brown area with rounded spaces for the lobes. While at first sight this was unsettling, the lack of brain was actually comforting in a strange way. It is so clear that a person cannot function without a brain that to know our cadaver doesn't have one removes her human-ness and alive-ness.

But it also leaves a hollow feeling. I can see how easy it is for health professionals to focus on the body and not on the person. Anatomy class forwards this conversion of perspectives.

–Rebecca

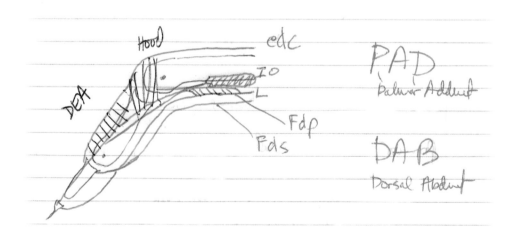

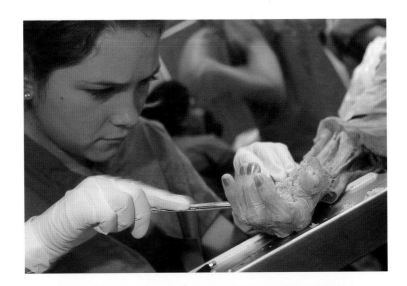

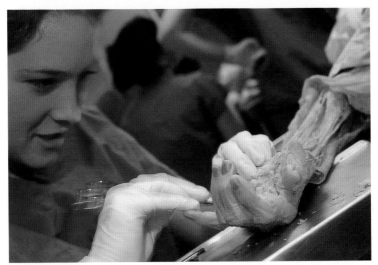

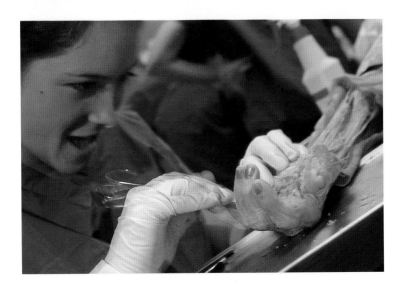

Thirteen outstretched arms greet me. The bodies on which we have worked for the last two weeks are all covered by white sheets except for the neck, the shoulder, and the arm.

Over the microphone, Professor Weber explains how [the practicum] is going to work. We will get a minute and a half to view whatever needs to be identified, and then move on to the rest area next to the body to write our answers.

A bell rings and it starts. Fifty-two living circle around the thirteen dead, and as many light boxes. We bend down over the little tag, trace the thin black string that emanates from it, stare for a minute and a half at the body part tied to the string, and then move on. Nerves on edge try to recall the names of nerves that have stopped stressing about the trite and the mundane long ago. Most of us have completely blocked out the body attached to the part in question. There is an ulnar nerve, a radial artery, a brachialis muscle, but no dead body.

In this macabre game of musical chairs, with the music replaced by timed silence punctuated by a ringing bell, I make my way to my cadaver. Even though I can only see a part of his forearm, I have no trouble discerning that he is mine.

Lateral Antebrachial Cutaneous. The nerve that supplies the lateral aspect of the forearm with sensory and sympathetic enervation. I get it instantly, as if someone whispered it in my ear. Now I have three minutes to kill.

My thoughts wander off to what my guy is thinking. He has patiently coached me for the last two weeks. He has taught me how to reflect skin without damaging the muscles, how to separate the muscles without damaging the arteries, and how to trace the nerves without getting them confused with blood vessels. While I have been rushed and hesitant, he has been a personification of steadiness and patience. Every time I got bored, he uncovered a flap of skin to reveal something nifty and marvelous. What else could he be thinking of at this time? I am sure every fiber in his body is concentrated on a single-minded pursuit: he wants to help me. Even if that means whispering the answer in my ear.

The rude bell pulls me out my thoughts and sends me scampering down the circle. Another hour of wandering about and I am done.

The grades are posted the next day. Of the thirteen questions on anatomy, I got twelve right. I almost feel like I failed someone on one of those tables. But twelve out of thirteen isn't bad, I say to myself, especially for a guy who used to program computers just five months ago. The eternity that preceded me doesn't care about my first Anatomy grade. It won't matter to the eternity that follows me. But for the time being I am happy. With the help of the dead, I have survived my first lab practical. I know the guy on Table 5 is smiling.

–Rajiv

Previous page: Katie (right) studying with a classmate at a local café.

Students move around the room during their first practicum.

I feel pretty different now from a week or two ago. Anatomy has been becoming a progressively positive influence in my life—well, maybe not positive, but it doesn't send chills up my spine and shudders through my body the way it used to. I guess the biggest factor in this turnaround was just finally realizing, "Hey, I can *do* this." The realization came at some point during my non-stop study weekend. Maybe it was the lack of sleep, or the hospital cafeteria food that caused this epiphany. The realization solidified during the practical exam, where I walked around in a semi-dream state, amazing myself with the knowledge base that I had acquired. Of course there are ten more weeks of Anatomy to study for and struggle through, but at least I have one good practical under my scrubs.

The studying experience was *very* intense. I couldn't function outside of the anatomy lab—my laundry went neglected, my refrigerator stayed empty, my bed went unmade. I wore the same scrubs every day.

After the practical, I did four loads of laundry and went food shopping. It was such a relief.

Now we're starting the thorax—the heart, lungs, etc.—the casing in which the life apparatus of my cadaver was held. It's a lot more personal than the arms. I'm looking forward to it, I think....

–Carrie

Hilary using her own arm as reference during the first exam.

There's so much to know, but I'm trying not to worry about it. It's so overwhelming sometimes, but if I give in to that feeling and try to learn absolutely everything, I know I'll lose it. And this experience, which is essential to medical school but still pretty awful, is just not worth losing my mind over. I made a decision before entering medical school that I won't let it change or destroy me. So I'm plugging along and trying to let go after a certain point. I'm still studying all day until 10:30 or 11 pm. I'll pass and I'll be a good doctor, regardless.

I went running with a classmate on Monday, and as we started talking, I was totally surprised by how much the whole Anatomy exercise still bothers me. It's pretty awful. But I'm so afraid to really talk about how it bothers me because I'm afraid it will undo me and I won't be able to go in and dissect. As far as participation goes, I've been okay since that first day, and I don't want to regress.

When I approach the body and see it oozing formaldehyde or see hair on the edge of the demolished scalp on top of it, I get really bothered. But when I narrow my view to the small area we're examining, I become interested and fascinated, and I want to learn all the important structures, enervation, and blood supply. It's pretty strange to flip back and forth like that.

–Andria

THE THORAX 2

Last night I had my first dream involving Gross Anatomy since class began over two weeks ago. I dreamt of my old apartment on Central Park West, where I lived during high school. I was now an adult and having a Christmas party.... As more and more people arrived, I found myself standing over a cadaver which was lying flat on a wooden table, draped with a clean, pressed white sheet. Only the thoracic region was exposed. I was meticulously teasing out the phrenic nerve so that it would be aesthetically presented for all of my guests. It was as if I were making a last-minute adjustment to a still-life arrangement carefully placed on a mahogany side table. Lynette [Cornell's professional dissector] and my TA, Bonnie, were creating beautiful delicate patterns with the lungs, like thoughtfully arranged hors d'oeuvres. It was clear however, that the anatomy was just for the partygoers to marvel at.

As new guests arrived, I pushed my way down the hall with my gloved hands held high in the air so that no one would expect me to shake their hands as I greeted them. My father arrived with his closest friend, a man in his late seventies for whom making his way out of his apartment to attend my Christmas party was a great effort. I hugged and kissed him hello and thanked him for coming, but it was clear he wanted to leave as soon as he had arrived. He apologized for having to go so quickly, but he said, "Not to worry, I will stay longer next time for your Nietzsche party in the spring." And then he left.

When I awoke, I had that distinctly satisfying feeling of just having had a fabulous dream remembered in great detail. I thought of how in my dream I had captured this particularly paradoxical moment in my life where I am close to both death and birth, and of the careful, meticulous preparations I am making with regard to both. What surprised me was the festive context of a party.

But I also could not escape the "Nietzsche party"—the idea that in this endeavor of learning the body, God is dead, and I am looking and probing where I should not, in regions that are only meant for God's eyes.

–Michael

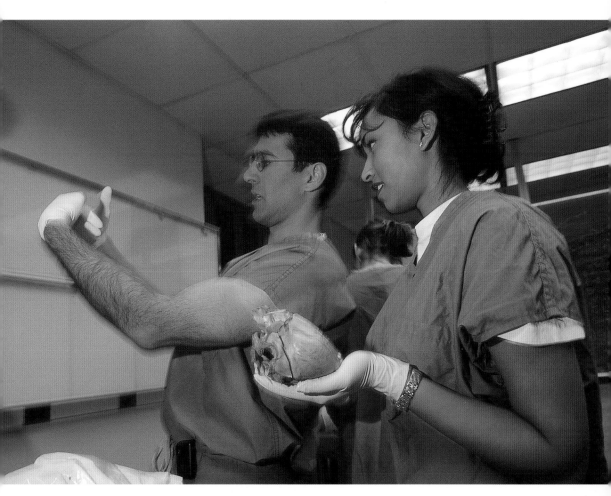

Tara, heart in hand, talking to her TA.

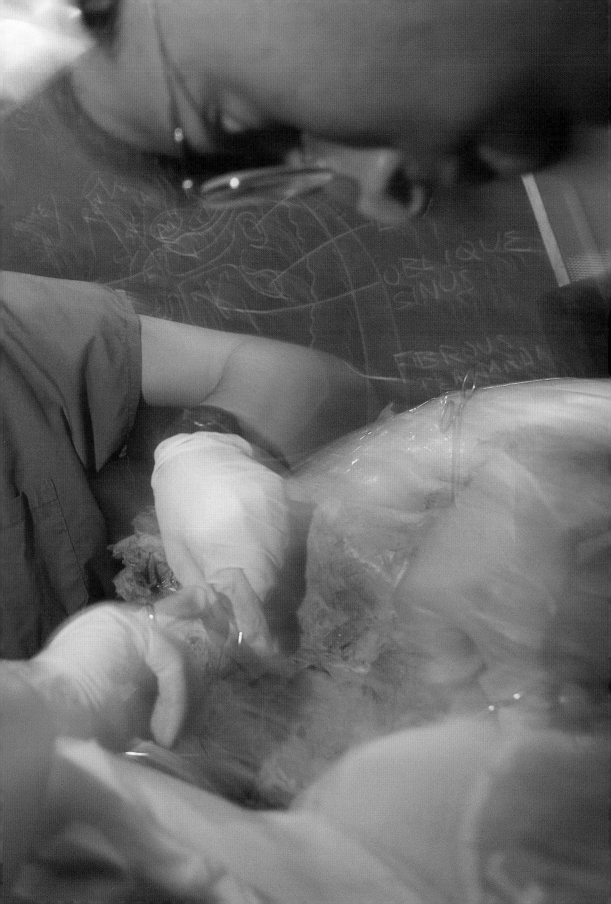

Oftentimes, when I stand back from the anatomy table I see my classmates huddling around the cadavers as NASA scientists might gather around newly-discovered aliens. Of course these are not aliens, but reflections of ourselves. This self-discovery is the privilege of Anatomy. With fascination, we hold between our fingers and dissect out that which makes us tick.

It is difficult at these times not to reflect upon the similarities between our own bodies and the cold cadavers before us. The heart that we hold in our hands once beat as strongly as the ones within us. The vessels, now dry and collapsed, are shadows of the bustling highways of blood flowing to the tips of our own fingers. We lie in bed and feel our own hearts pulsing within our own bellies. After touching the spongy lung, which rebounds with ease after a gentle squeeze, we draw deep breaths and picture the dramatic expansion and contraction within our own chest walls. With each muscle, we memorize, flex, and extend our own, noting the range of motion. In Anatomy exams, our bodies are our cheat sheets.

–Hilary

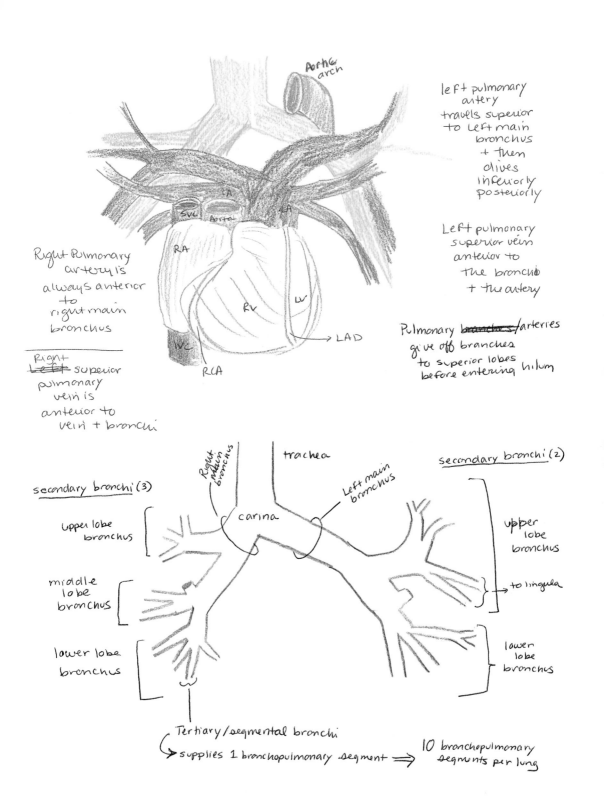

Aorta arch

left pulmonary artery travels superior to Left main bronchus + then dives inferiorly posteriorly

Left pulmonary superior vein anterior to the bronchus + the artery

PA

SVC

Aorta

LA

RA

PA

RV

LV

→ LAD

VC

RCA

Right Pulmonary artery is always anterior to right main bronchus

~~Right~~
~~Left~~ superior pulmonary vein is anterior to vein + bronchi

Pulmonary ~~branches~~/arteries give off branches to superior lobes before entering hilum

trachea

Right main bronchus

Left main bronchus

secondary bronchi (2)

carina

secondary bronchi (3)

upper lobe bronchus

upper lobe bronchus

middle lobe bronchus

→ to lingula

lower lobe bronchus

lower lobe bronchus

Tertiary/segmental bronchi
⤷ supplies 1 bronchopulmonary segment ⟹ 10 bronchopulmonary segments per lung

We cut through the ribs on both sides of the chest, bringing the incisions together below the Adam's apple. We then reflected the top, which was still attached to the body at the diaphragm. Underneath, cradled between the two lungs, lay the master organ—the heart—about which just as much has been written in romance novels and poetry as in medicine. It is the symbol of human kindness, love, and compassion. When you really want something, it longs. When you are moved to tears, it cries. Today was our chance to dissect it.

It took a couple of incisions on the two large veins that drain into the right atrium in order to detach the heart from the venous system. Another large cut at the aorta, and the heart was decoupled from its circulatory loop. Two more deep cuts on the sides and it was free from the lungs. I gingerly pulled it out, and there it was, in the palm of my hand. It wasn't much to look at: a leathery bag of muscle with excised tubes projecting from all directions.

All this hue and cry about this bag of muscle. Frankly, I was disappointed. I walked over to Darlene's table. Her cadaver is a very heavy man. She was busy digging out the blood supply that feeds the heart muscle.

"Rajiv, feel this," she said to me.

I ran my finger over the left circumflex artery (a major vessel that supplies a good part of the left side of the heart muscle). It was not smooth, but rather bumpy with knots in it. These were the places where atherosclerotic plaque had calcified and hardened.

Then I noticed the rib cage, which had been cut open on three sides. His fifth and sixth ribs on both sides were broken at the point where they attach to the sternum (the bone in the middle of the chest). A big, dark-brown blood clot had formed on the inside wall of his chest. With these clues, it was not hard to put his story together: with lack of exercise and a lifetime of eating junk food, the grease from hamburgers and fries built up in his coronary arteries. Slowly, his arteries became narrower and narrower, hardened by the plaque that formed inside of them.

It must have been painful for him before the end. He must have suffered carrying his weight around, climbing stairs, or just walking from the bed to the bathroom—a dull, throbbing pain in the chest. Months, maybe years of this suffering and then, Bam! He was on the floor clutching his chest. Someone tried to resuscitate him by CPR. That person must have tried really hard, for his ribs had been broken. But it was in vain. After a lifetime of coping, his bag of muscle had given up.

Suddenly, the immense beauty of this seemingly simple organ was driven home. It never gives up. We run, and it races to keep pace. We sit down, but it keeps going. We abuse it by pushing all sorts of garbage through it, but it still keeps going.

Maybe the literary folks have it wrong. Maybe the heart should be used as metaphor not for love and romance, but for perseverance.

–Rajiv

Previous page: Guest cardiologist discussing heart structure with students.

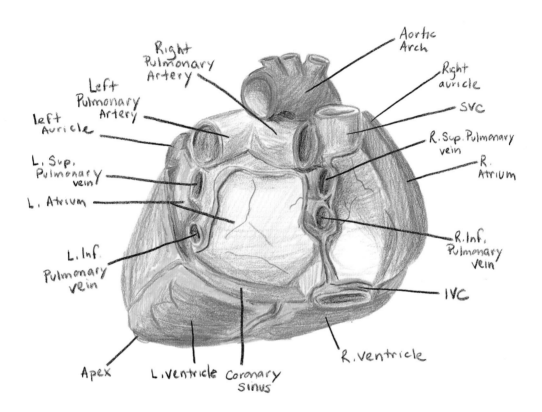

Right Pulmonary Artery

Left Pulmonary Artery

left Auricle

L. Sup. Pulmonary vein

L. Atrium

L. Inf. Pulmonary vein

Apex

L. Ventricle

Coronary sinus

Aortic Arch

Right auricle

SVC

R. Sup. Pulmonary vein

R. Atrium

R. Inf. Pulmonary vein

IVC

R. Ventricle

I guess I'm sort of at the point of writer's block, or maybe thinker's block, if there is such a thing. We're well into Gross Anatomy now, and instead of developing and possibly blossoming, my thoughts on the experience have hit a dead end. It's not that I'm purposely trying not to think about it. I'm trying—in lab, in front of my computer, in my head. The initial shock and disgust are over and right now it seems almost routine to don hospital garb and make my way down to the lab. It's not unlike any other class, except maybe it smells sort of bad—but even the smell has become routine. I try to make the thoughts whirl around, but for some reason, they don't go anywhere.

We dissected the heart this week, and some people spoke about feeling a more personal side of their cadavers. I held the heart in my hand. In fact, I held two hearts in my hands, and even posed for the camera with them. But I didn't feel a "pang" of anything. No chills up my spine, no nauseous pit in my stomach. Just intellectual curiosity more than anything else.

Then one of my lab partners washed the dried blood out of our heart (I wonder what it means that I call our cadaver's heart "our heart") and simulated pumping, by opening and closing the valves. It was then I noticed that the heart was no longer beating. I guess I just hadn't thought about it before, too caught up in the learning process, too focused on finishing up the lab so I could get to lunch. Only three weeks ago, I was so sick after each lab that lunch did not even cross my mind.

What has happened? I suppose I have become comfortable, or at least reconciled to the reality of the next ten weeks. I don't like that. I don't like that I have stopped truly thinking about the experience, because there is still a lot to think about. These cadavers did once live, breathe, eat, and sleep before they so graciously donated their bodies to medicine. Their hearts did once beat. And I am still just a mere medical student, gently prying open human flesh with my scalpel and probe.

–Carrie

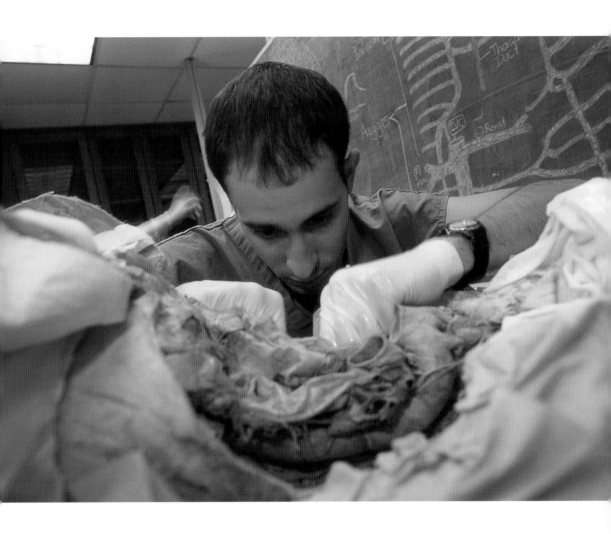

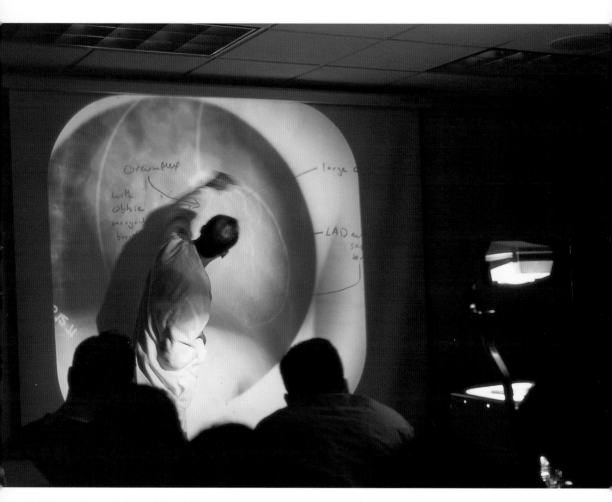

Exploring the heart during radiology lab.

When I first looked at the lungs lying in the chest, I was astounded by their incredible size. They took up most of the space there, completely enveloping the heart and creeping up into the neck. It seems that the other organs found in this area must compete with the lungs for space.

I reached in to grab a lung. It was so soft and resilient. It felt like a sponge, but even softer, and no matter how hard I squeezed it seemed to find its way back to its original shape.

As I looked at the lungs and held them, I thought of my mother and father. They both smoked cigarettes when I was a child. My mother knew it was hurting her health and tried to quit. I remember how hard that was for her. She would quit for a day, then start up again. A week, then start up again. A month. Three months. Six months, then start up again. It took my mother three years to stop smoking. My father only smokes occasionally, and often goes weeks between smokes. The surgeons told us that it takes years and years of abuse to develop bad lungs. So I'm hoping it doesn't catch up to my father....

–Marcus

My classmate Hilary and I believe that when it comes to radiology, the only way to learn is through "repetition, repetition, repetition." Only then do the gray blobs take on meaning, making it possible for us to anticipate what they will do, where they will travel, and with what they will intersect.

So we sacrificed a beautiful, sunny, Saturday afternoon to study for the upcoming exam on the thorax. We entered the lab laughing and calling out "O.K., who are the nerds down here on such a beautiful day?" Imagine our surprise; we were the only ones.

Normally used for announcements during Anatomy lab, the microphone now hung on its wall-hook, a little limp, a little lonely. It tempted us to serenade those on the tables around us.

With a glance at each other and a slight check to see if anyone was watching, we grabbed the microphone and sang a roaring rendition of "New York, New York" half expecting applause, or at least snickers. Only silence greeted us. Unswayed by the lack of enthusiasm from our audience, we thanked them for their attention and launched into another song.

"So, Rebecca, do you think they liked us? They were a little passive," Hilary joked after we'd finished.

"Of course!" I said. "They loved us! Couldn't you tell by the sparkle in their eyes? Who wouldn't want a little singing to liven up the place? They must be bored out of their minds just lying there watching their nerves be frayed, their fat unceremoniously scooped out, their arteries sliced, and their hearts held up for all the world to see."

We returned the microphone to its hook and walked over to the light boxes, slowly returning to the black, white, and mostly gray world of radiology.

"You know," Hilary said, "if they wanted to overtake us, they could. There are so many of them."

Just at that moment, a loud clatter rose from behind us. Startled, we turned around. The microphone lay on the floor. We rationalized that it had been improperly placed on the hook. Although we never verbalized it, we couldn't quite shake the eerie feeling that at least one of the cadavers wanted a little more respect.

–Rebecca

Entering the lab for the second practicum: the thorax.

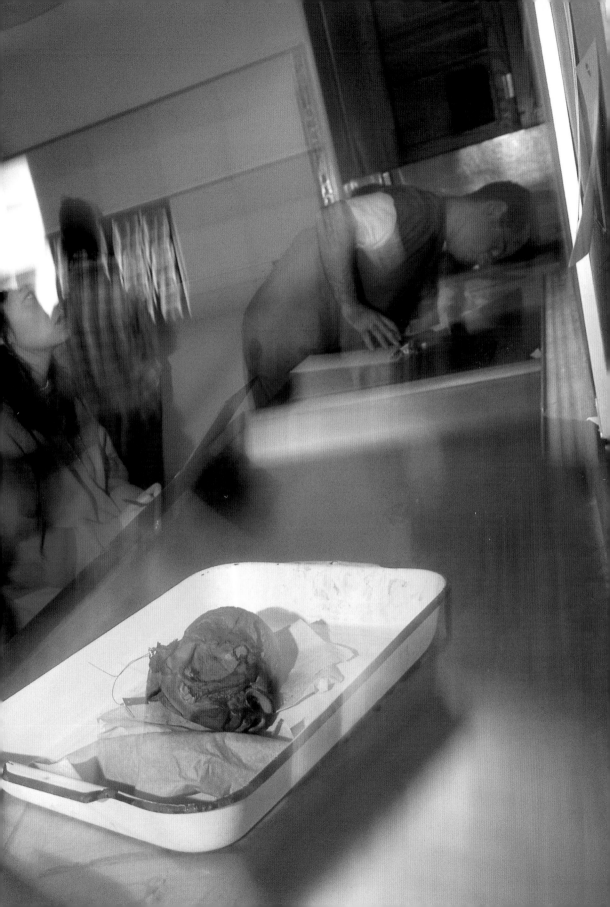

We're on to the abdomen now. It really seems like the "heart" of the body. There's so much in this one compartment. I just feel like it's all put together so perfectly and I don't want to displace things, like the intestines. They are coiled up to fit exactly within the space they're assigned to. It's just so amazing that the body can do the complex activities of digestion and detoxification and energy disbursement with these seemingly simple tubes and clusters of tissue. Really, it's just incredible.

–Andria

Previous page: Rajiv standing before a heart in a tray during the second exam.

THE ABDOMEN 3

Our first day in the abdomen, and already I feel overwhelmed and behind. All the layers of the abdominal wall, their embryological origin, and the regions they form have become a blur in my mind. The simple things that I thought I knew now seem difficult to comprehend. Even the looming fear that I may not understand it all doesn't motivate me. I miss the excitement of the thorax. I miss the thrill of holding the heart in my hand, cutting open a lung. The liver, intestine, and stomach don't seem as exciting or as essential as the heart and the lungs. I hope my enthusiasm and interest in anatomy does not fade completely.

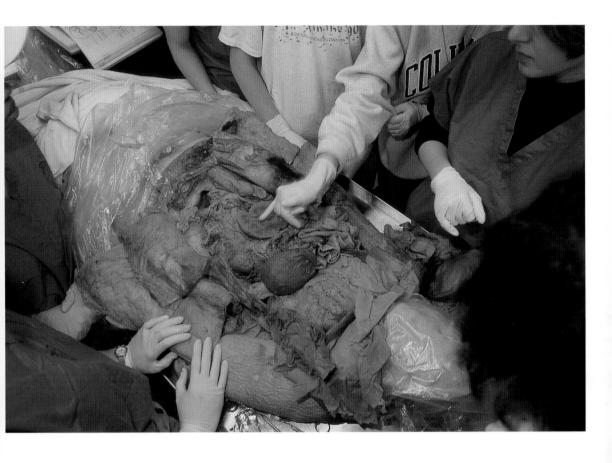

One interesting part of today's dissection was the scrotum. The scrotum is part of the abdominal region because the testicles descend from behind the abdomen, and as they travel downward, they accumulate layers of the abdominal wall. I began this dissection with hesitation. It was strange to make slices through each of these layers and then to find the testes inside. The most interesting aspect however, was the way every male in my lab group ran from the table as I took the scalpel to the scrotal covering. As much as we try to forget that these bodies are human, some things cannot be masked.

–Tara

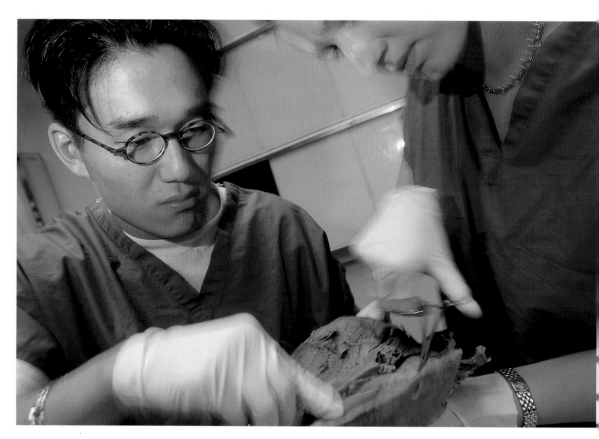

Hansoo Michael (left) inspecting his cadaver's liver.

Labels on diagram: Middle colic, SMA, Marginal artery, Vasa Recta, p. 108 Moore differences of jejunum + ileum, IMA, left colic ascending branch descending branch, Right colic, Ileocolic, body of pancreas, SMA, left renal vein, uncinate process panc., sigmoid, 3rd part of duod, SMA, Intestine

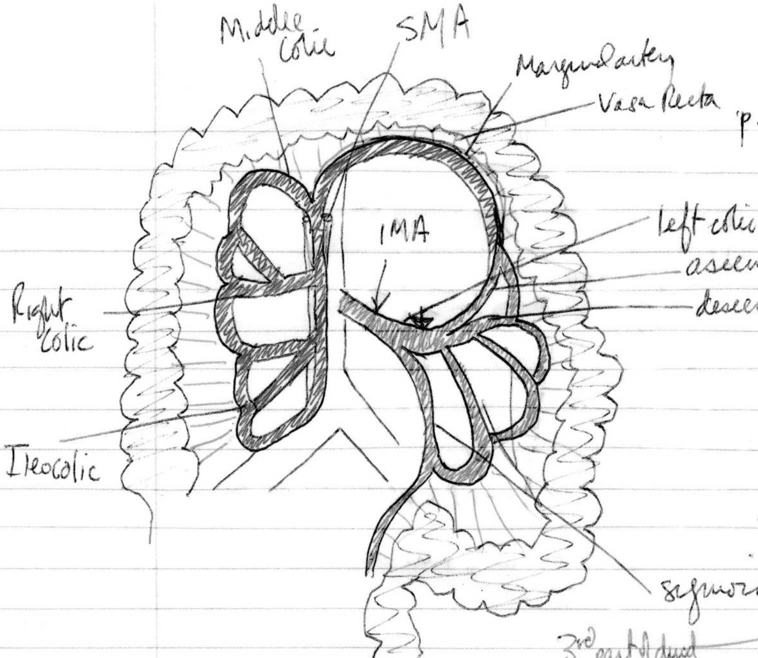

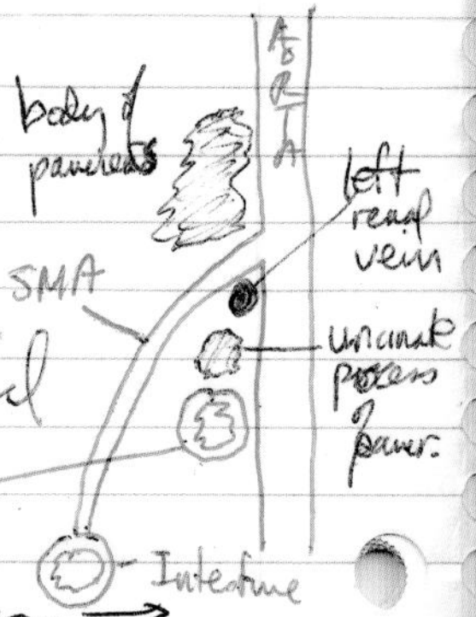

SMA - 85% of bowel (from part of duodenum
   all of S.I. and part of large colon)
IMA - 15% of bowel (last part of colon)

appendix - origin is always in posterior aspect
   of cecum
        - trace back 3 bands (muscular) + all
   converge on appendix
   — blood supply

   65% - retroperi
   31% - cross pelvic brim

	Size	Wall	Vasc	Vasa Recta	Arcades	Mesentric
Jejunum:	2-4cm	Thick	Greater	Long	Long loops	Less
Ileum:	2-3cm	Thin	Less	Short	Many short loops	More

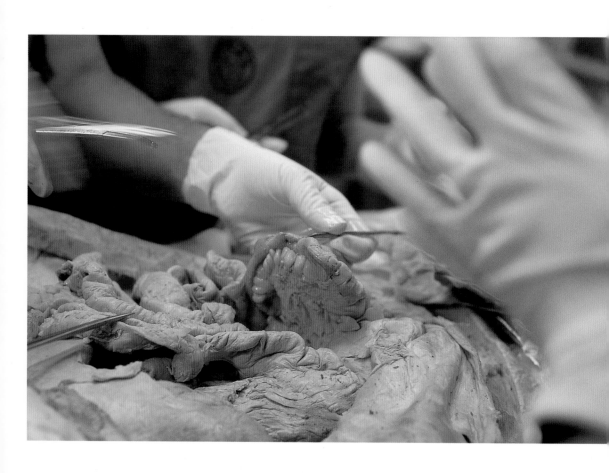

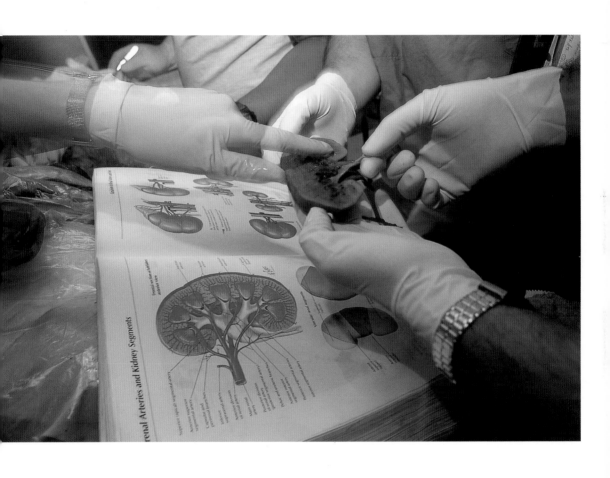

Is that pizza I ate an hour ago having a tough time bending around the splenic flexure of the large bowel, or is it gliding along with little effort? Is it in my stomach, where acids are breaking it down, or in the jejunum, where some absorption is going on?

I love the gut! I can't believe how amazing it is to actually see the inside of the body in all its glory. Now, after having dissected the digestive system, all I think about when I eat or drink something is where the food is in my intestine at any given time, and what, physiologically, is happening to it.

Even more intriguing, and a little embarrassing, is that whenever I have to go to the bathroom the same thoughts enter my mind and I think about all of the things involved with the process of defecation. I guess that's glorifying it a little bit, but I'm not kidding, this is how I spend my time on the pot these days.

For some reason, I particularly love the small and large intestine. When I dissected these two structures and had my hands full of intestine, I felt like this was what dissection is all about. For lack of a better phrase, I felt like I was "really getting my hands dirty." Because these structures are so big (i.e., bigger than nerves and vessels), and they aren't as fragile as some of the plexuses or arterial trunks, we were able to really twist, turn, and manipulate them so as to gain a better understanding of the spatial relationships within the abdomen.

Another thing I found a little amusing was that after working on a given body, inevitably the intestines became all tangled and out of proper placement, and it took a minute or two at the end of class to reposition everything properly.

In short, I loved the abdomen.

–David

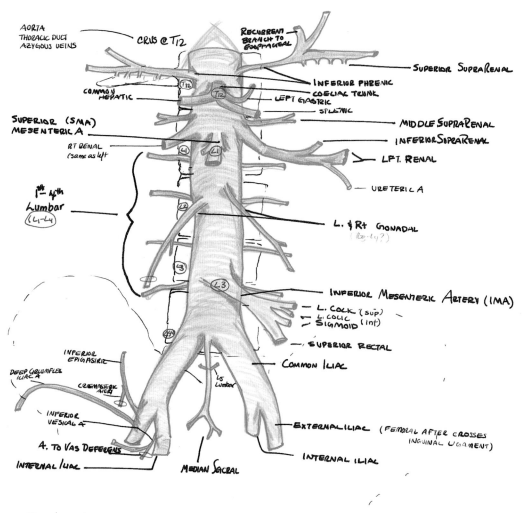

AORTA
THORACIC DUCT
AZYGOUS VEINS

CRUS @ T12

RECURRENT
BRANCH TO
ESOPHAGEAL

SUPERIOR SUPRARENAL

T12

COMMON
HEPATIC

T12

INFERIOR PHRENIC
COELIAC TRUNK
LEFT GASTRIC
SPLENIC

MIDDLE SUPRARENAL

SUPERIOR (SMA)
MESENTERIC A

INFERIOR SUPRARENAL

RT RENAL
(same as left

L1

L1

LFT. RENAL

URETERIC A

1ST-4TH
Lumbar
(L1-L4)

L2

L. & Rt GONADAL
(L2-L4?)

L3

L3

INFERIOR MESENTERIC ARTERY (IMA)

L. COLIC (SUP)
L. COLIC (INT)
SIGMOID

4th

SUPERIOR RECTAL

INFERIOR
EPIGASTRIC

DEEP CIRCUMFLEX
ILIAC A

CREMASTERIC
ARTERY

L5
Lumbar

COMMON ILIAC

INFERIOR
VESICAL A

EXTERNAL ILIAC (FEMORAL AFTER CROSSES
INGUINAL LIGAMENT)

A. TO VAS DEFERENS

INTERNAL ILIAC

MEDIAN SACRAL

INTERNAL ILIAC

○ = to scrotum

SMA

MIDDLE COLIC

RT. COLIC

ILEOCOLIC

COLIC

ILEAL

APPENDICULAR

ABDOMINAL BRANCHES OF THE AORTA

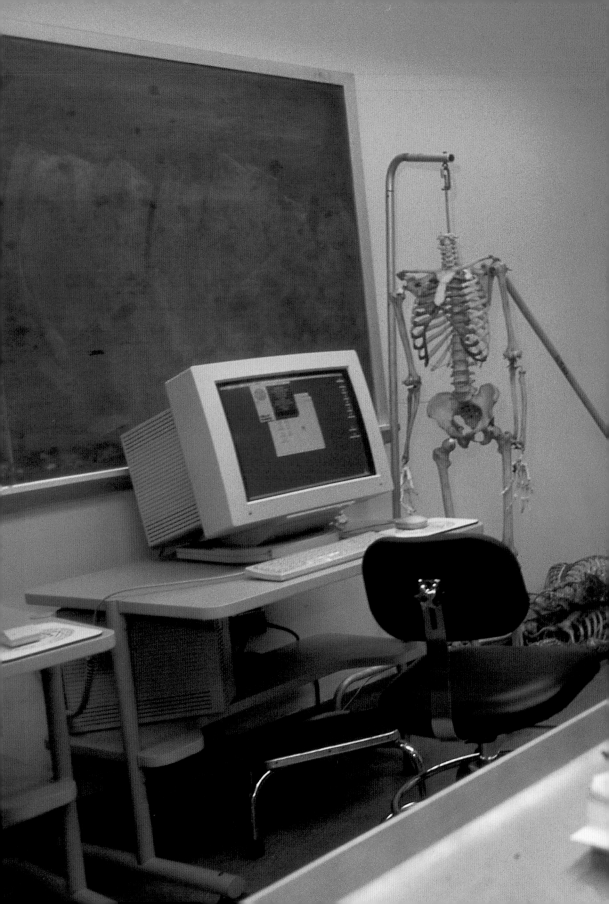

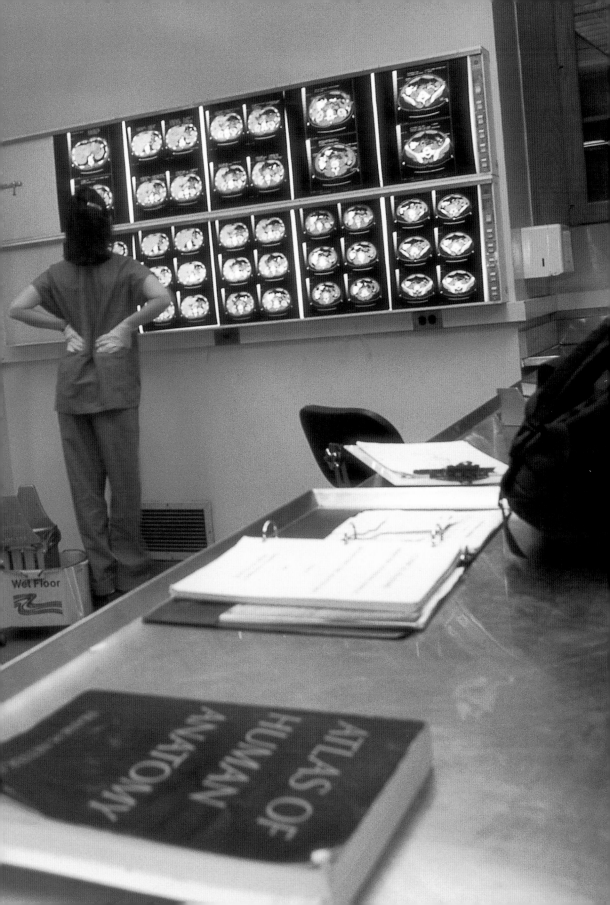

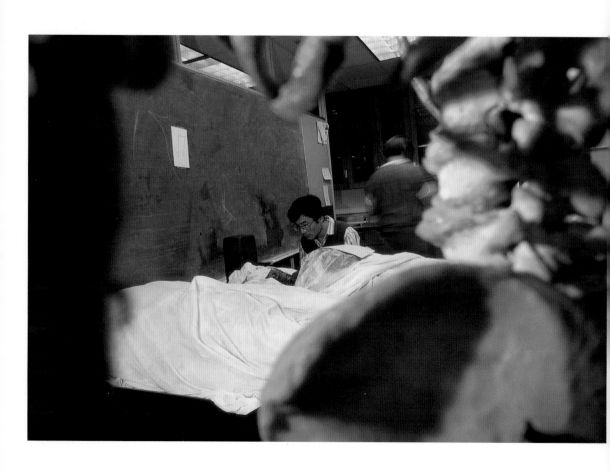

Extra time at an exam rest station.

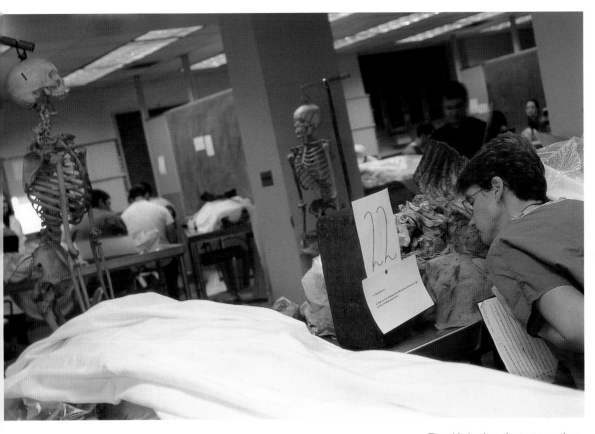

Then it's back to the test questions.

The Class Show featuring a skit about the Anatomy experience (left), and a hospital scrubs fashion show that ended with a striptease (above).

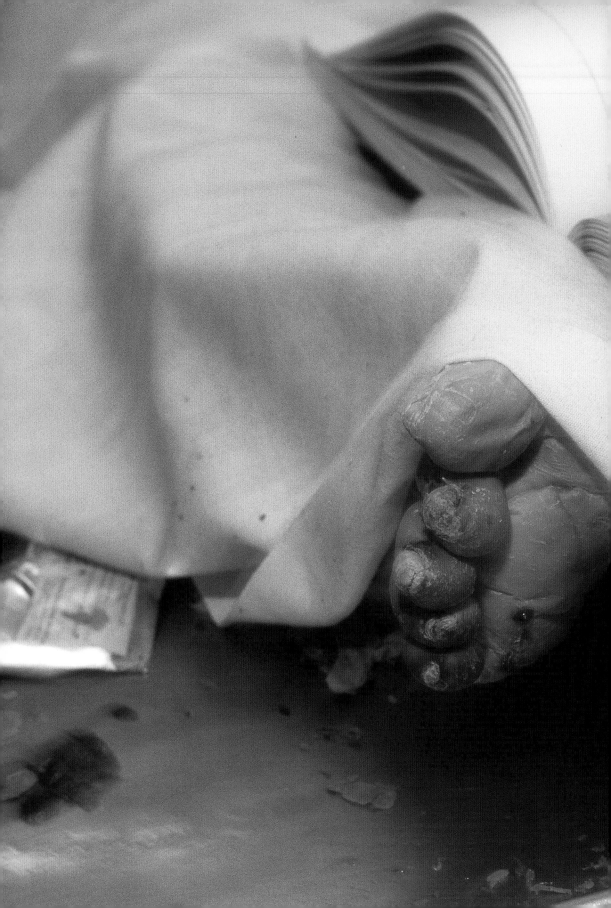

I entered the lab at 9 pm to prepare for the practical on the abdomen. A bizarre scene confronted me. The legs of each cadaver had been pulled apart and tied to a rod to keep them separated. The rod was pulled up and its two ends were tied to the wall above the head. This way, the legs were both raised and separated. The main body, from the head to the buttocks, was still on the dissection table, so when I stood at the table near the legs, I saw a vertical V-shape formed by the legs. When I stood to the side, the body looked like an oddly proportioned "L." It was clear that the lab was getting ready to dissect the pelvis.

A few teaching assistants were still there, finishing up their prosections for the next day's demonstration. All were well prepared for a long night: the coffee pot was going, and portable lamps were drawn close to them to illuminate the gluteal region. Meticulously, the TAs pecked away at the fat surrounding the genitals and the lower pelvis, carefully preserving the fragile, fishing-wire-like nerves that make this area so exquisitely sensitive in the living. While alive, this fat existed in the cadaver's body in a near-liquid state, a cushion for his or her seat. Now, solidified, it fills up the crevices of the cadaver's pelvis and the buttocks.

I glanced at all this while walking to the back of the room to the computer terminals. I had to learn the vessels and the nerves of this area, along with their three-dimensional organization, before I could appreciate them in the cadaver. Pretty soon I was absorbed in the 3-D computerized details of the human body, completely oblivious to my bizarre surroundings.

Something has happened to me in the last three months. Before, I would have hung around the bodies, gawked at the labia major, and pestered the TAs about every little nerve they exposed. I do not do that any more. It's not that Gross Anatomy has deadened my curiosity or dulled my sense of wonder. Quite the contrary. I have come to realize that the human body is a mysterious machine, dead or alive. I have realized that there is a discipline and an order to learning human anatomy.

Staring at an exposed nerve plexus, or a set of crisscrossing blood vessels, is somewhat like looking at the motherboard of a personal computer. It bewilders you, but does not teach you anything. You have to know the circuit diagram beforehand. Only then can you appreciate the real complexity of the machine.

–Rajiv

THE PELVIS 4

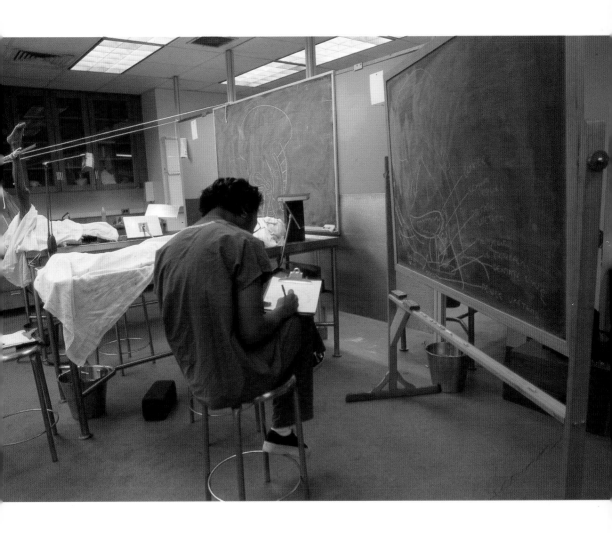

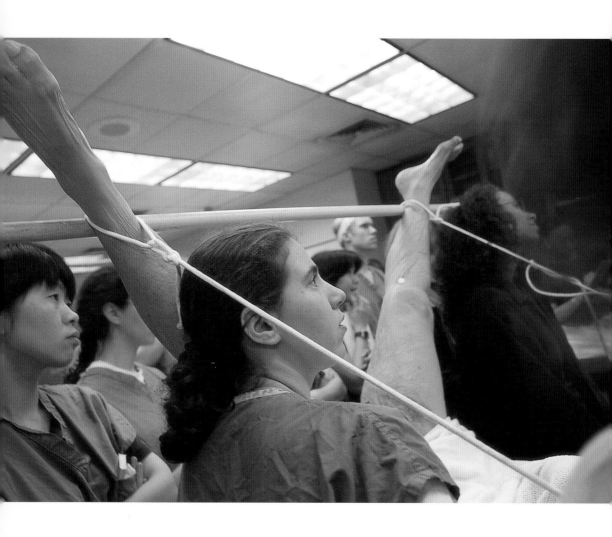

We have been dissecting the pelvis this past week. As always, the apprehension of dissecting a new region of the body has disappeared. Seeing legs flying in the air and penises cut open has no strong effect anymore.

Every day I become more immune to the fact that we are dissecting a human body. Every day I lose sight of the fact that the person I am cutting open was someone's father, brother, son, friend. I am seeing parts of this human being that no other person has seen. I was able to hold his heart. I saw him in positions that were violating. I view him as a cadaver. I forget that all the parts of a dead body's anatomy are also part of me. The dissection of the pelvic region has confirmed these changes in me. Once again, the cadaver is a tool for learning.

–Tara

■ ■ ■

The pelvis is close to the leg and the leg is close to the foot, so that means we're almost done with this class—which is a very good thing.

I feel like I've learned so much that I can't imagine that there will be any "new" material to learn after this year.

Dissecting the pelvis is the first part of the body since Anatomy began that seems a bit "yucky." It's strange, but I think our culture really teaches us to think that way. It also feels a little weird to talk openly about all the anatomy and normal body functions of this area.

I'm just glad we're not including a pelvic exam on our classmates as part of our physical diagnosis class. That would be much more than I could handle.

–Andria

It's amazing how easily certain words roll off our tongues now without a moment's hesitation. When a classmate and I discuss pelvic anatomy over lunch in a restaurant, we find ourselves getting interesting glances. We aren't careful enough to censor.

It was the thick rope and the vulnerable positions that conjured up images of a torture chamber. Anatomy lab, first day of the pelvic dissection: bodies tied up by their ankles with legs spread wide, exposing the genital region. I felt uncomfortable standing next to the ropes that were tied from the ceiling to the ankles. Why would there be a need for restraint? They are dead.

The bodies that were spared this fate were instead sliced literally in half—hemisected right down the middle. After seeing that, the ropes didn't seem so bad. While I was in the lab, I imagined the cartoons and action movies in which the protagonist gets tied to a moving belt headed straight for a serrated round saw. Just before the edge slices the guy in two, he breaks free and escapes in the nick of time. When I looked at the hemisected cadavers, all I could think was, they didn't escape.

Of course the hemisection procedure wasn't performed exactly that way. But today the bodies were undeniably changed forever. Earlier in the course, we could patch things up—put the liver neatly back in place, place the heart in its spot, close the flaps of skin, make the body look whole again. But now, with legs literally removed from bodies, there is no turning back.

–Hilary

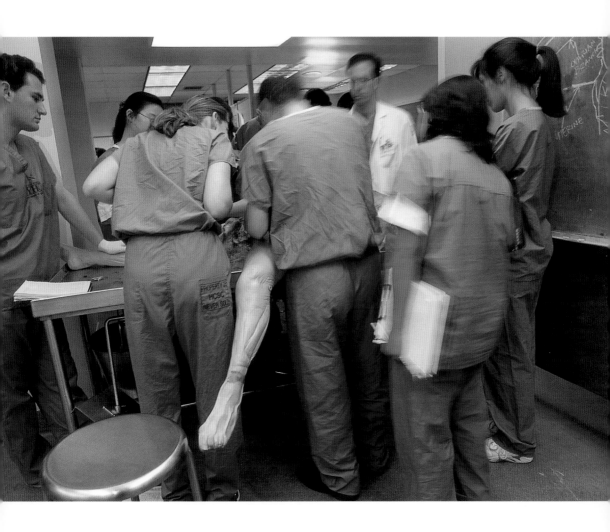

Lately, I've been thinking a lot about my college days (over 12 years ago, when I was an art major). Crowding in front of the light boxes five deep to view the x-rays, CT scans, and MRIs has reminded me of how we used to group together to study slides for upcoming art history exams. Back then, I always felt slightly electrified, hyper-focused, almost giddy with the energy flowing among us as we jammed in tight around a light box. In the eerie light reflected through the colored slides of paintings from the sixteenth and seventeenth centuries, there was intimacy and excitement. I think the combination of learning about art and being twenty years old was a powerful one.

Now I don't feel the same romance, but there still is a sense of camaraderie. It is as if we have joined a medieval order and are monks in training. We descend into a grotto in full habit of green/blue to study sacred backlit images. I try to conjure up comparisons with paintings that I know. The abstractionists from any decade of the twentieth century come to mind, but I cannot find a connection. Instead, I feel like I am studying twelfth-century illuminated manuscripts in order to memorize their content and gather their meaning. Even though the technology is very new, I feel like these images are old texts—the body has not changed much in 10,000 years; its secrets beneath the skin are the same.

–Michael

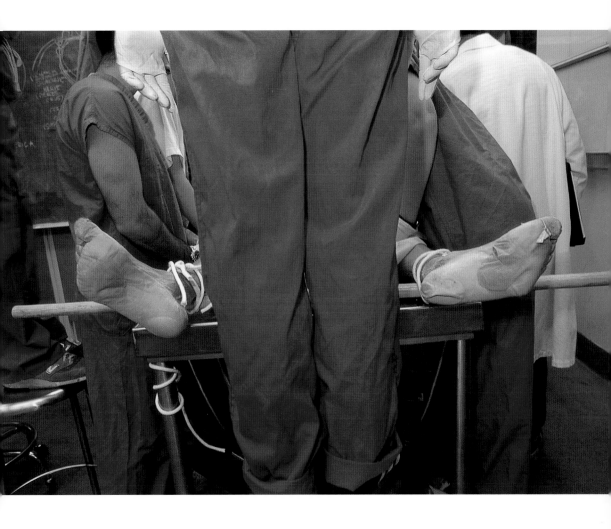

Casually, when speaking to one another, we refer to the cadavers in a possessive manner: "Come check out the hypertrophied right ventricle on *my* cadaver" or "Does *your* body have an appendix?" When you stop and think about it, it is strange to refer to the bodies in such a way. Once Jane Doe, now a teaching tool as cold and lifeless and inanimate as *my* microscope.

She is our silent yet invaluable teacher, selflessly offering all that anyone has to give. I think I appreciate her selflessness most at the beginning of each lab session. She lies on the table, like a perpetual surgery patient who never gets sutures or sent home. We focus on the virgin territory of the week, that which is untouched, uncut, unmarked except for the hematoma left from the IV, or the birthmark, or the thin, dark hairs covering the wrinkles and stretched skin.

Like children venturing onto a snow-covered yard to make the first angels in the powder, our scalpel enters the skin and quickly and smoothly, the incision is made. These cuts won't ever heal.

We are all possessive of our own bodies. I look down at my hands; they are like old friends. I have known them my whole life, depended upon them to express, write, caress, scratch, hold, throw, and type (as I am doing now). I feel the same way about my entire body. Yet here I am, taking a knife to this woman's body parts, parts that she viewed as personal. I am destroying that wholeness forever. I realize she chose this destiny after death, yet I cannot help but feel a little guilty.

–Hilary

Understanding the pelvic region.

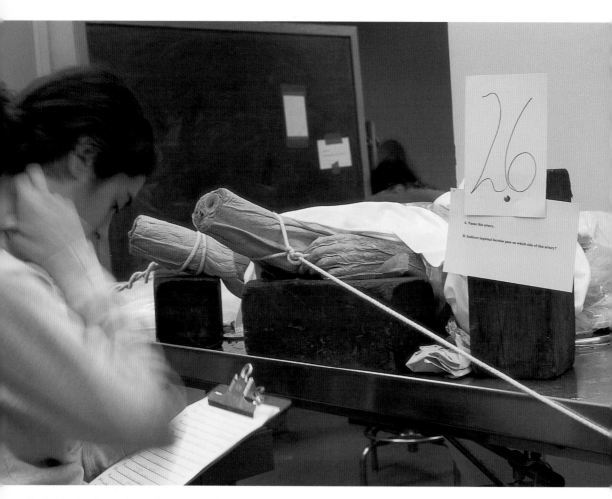

During the fourth practicum: the pelvis.

It was 12:15 pm, and the test on the pelvis was about to begin. I had just sat through two hours' worth of lecture and did not absorb a thing. I couldn't wait until the test was over so I could get into my bed. I was exhausted.

Before the test started, Dr. Weber asked me if I would be willing to post the answers as soon as our exam was over—just as the second group began their exam. I thought it would be nice to lend a helping hand, so I agreed. When the test was finally over, I was pleased with my performance. I did not know that the worst was yet to come.

As we handed in our papers, Dr. Weber announced to the class, "Marcus will be posting the answers upstairs in the educational center." I thought that if I could just get to my jacket quick enough and then get lost among the next group of students entering for their exam, I'd be home free. Well, I got to my jacket fairly quickly and made it out through the crowd in record time, but there were already two people waiting for me at the base of the staircase. Unbelievable. Before I knew it, three of the four answer sheets were taken out of my hands. Upstairs, I could not open the glass of the display case fast enough. As soon as I put one page up, everyone wanted me to move out of the way so they could see the answers. I was pressed up against the wall. I told them to stand back, but that did not work, so I quickly grabbed back all four pages and posted them while pushing people back with my elbows.

I heard screams of happiness along with curses of sadness. I left them all standing in front of the answer key and headed home.

–Marcus

We have been very respectful of her body for the most part, not like others in the lab who don't completely cover their bodies, or don't put the skin back in place when they're done for the day. One of the recent disturbing events was seeing the top half of a head in the lab during the exam with a fresh haircut artfully designed by one of my classmates, I'd guess at like 5 am while studying for the exam or something. I don't really know the story, but it bothered me. Other people laughed, but I didn't really think it was too cool.

–Andria

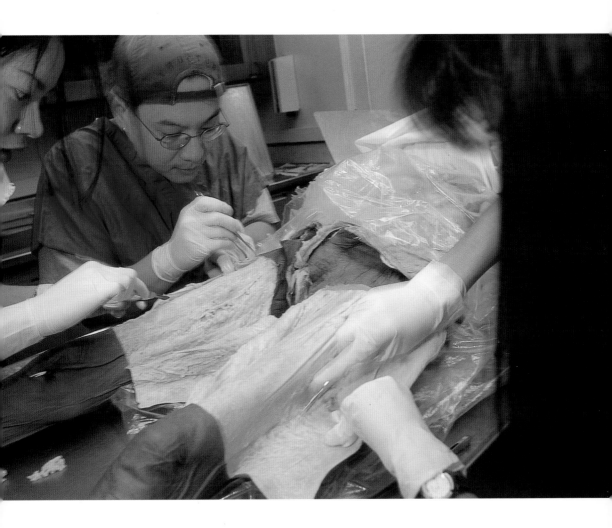

The power of habit is incredible. It is now two and a half months since we began Anatomy, and I feel unstartled by my cadaver, by all of the dead bodies, by the basement room and the ritual. Even the oily smell which coats me is acceptable, almost unnoticed, like a neighbor that has lived down the hall for a while. I don't think twice about the cutting or having lunch afterward without an intervening shower. I no longer draw silent comparisons between my cadaver's subcutaneous fascia and my son's unblemished face. Gross Anatomy has become one of the routine workings of my life, and by some sad equation, I am now wondering less about my cadaver's life, his routines, his visions, his loves, and his thought process which ultimately brought him to the anatomy lab.

In preparation for today's first lab of the lower limb, I felt nothing. It may be that after the grit and awe of handling his heart and lungs, the viscera of his abdomen, and his urogenital organs, my cadaver's anterior thigh was not very inspiring. I think I felt that there were no more secrets left to move me. I was wrong. It was the most profound day yet.

After seeing the prosection, I knew what I wanted to work on. I felt a powerful need to dissect out the right greater saphenous vein. I took my time and slowly cleaned it of all of its attachments to the surrounding tissue. I felt obliged to dissect it out beautifully, in homage to my cadaver, Stanley. The task was soothing. When I was through, it glistened perfectly, a milky-blue from the upper thigh all the way down to the medial knee. I backed away from the table and started to tremble. I thought of my father, who is still alive after two cardiac bypass surgeries. His own saphenous veins from both legs are miraculously part of his damaged heart's circulation. They are his vessels of life and are the reason he saw me graduate from high school, from college, get married, and have two children.

Today, I became aware of how close I was to losing my father and how miraculous it is that he is still alive. For this, in addition to all that I've had the great privilege to learn, I am most grateful to Stanley.

–Michael

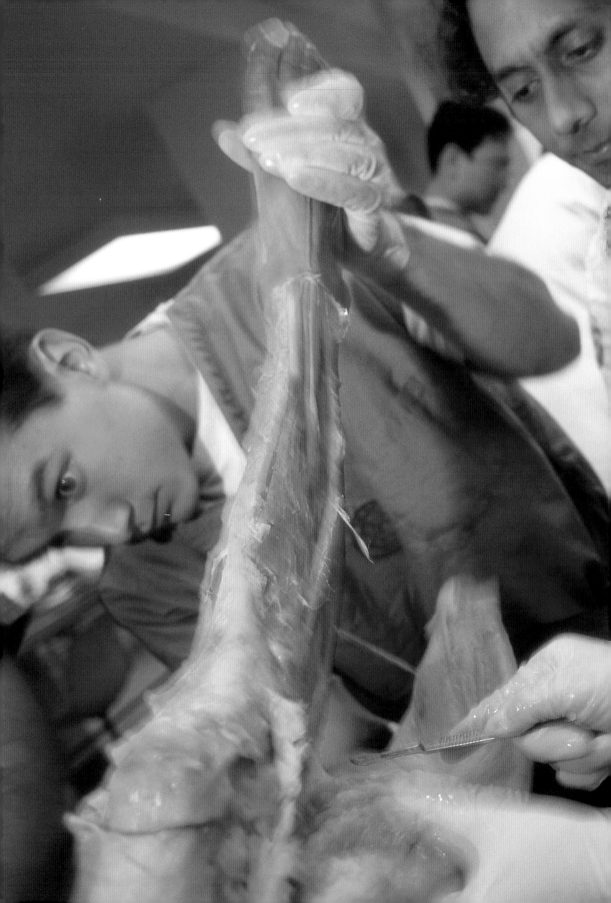

As we made our way down to the knee, something happened that I was not particularly ready for. While dissecting, we put pressure on the lower leg. As we pressed down, smelly juice came squirting out onto the table, the floor and, of course, onto us. Apparently, as we dissected down from the neck towards the legs, fluid from her fat had pooled in her legs. It was nice because we were all in intimate contact with the cadaver, but disgusting because of the horrible smell.

–Marcus

FEMUR

Head
Fovea of head
greater trochanter
neck
lesser trochanter
intertrochanteric line
shaft

Greater trochanter
intertrochanteric crest
lesser trochanter
gluteal tuberosty
pectineal line
linea aspera { medial lip, lateral lip }

lateral supracondyle line
medial supracondyle line

lateral epicondyle
medial epicondyle
medial condyle
Anterior
lateral condyle
Patellar surface

Medial epicondyle
Lateral epicondyle
Posterior
intercondylar fossa
medial condyle
lateral condyle

Femur
(fibular) lateral collateral ligament
PCL
ACL
lateral meniscus
tibia
tibial (medial) collateral ligament
medial meniscus
transverse ligament of knee
fibula
Tuberosity of tibia

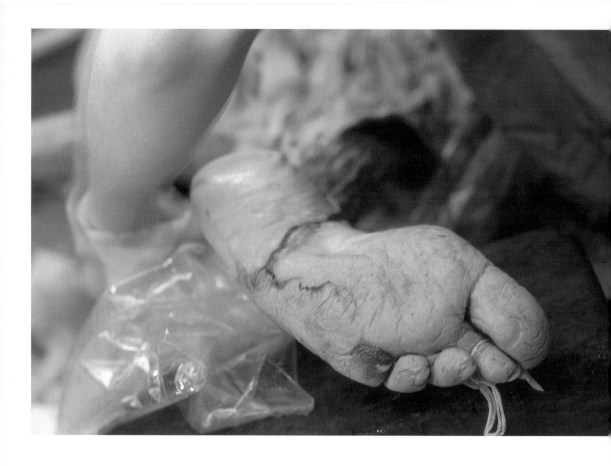

Mentally, it is tough cutting into the foot because I know how sensitive my own feet are. Cutting into any part of my body would hurt, but there is something about the feet (as there was about the hands) that makes me squirm at every poke.

–Marcus

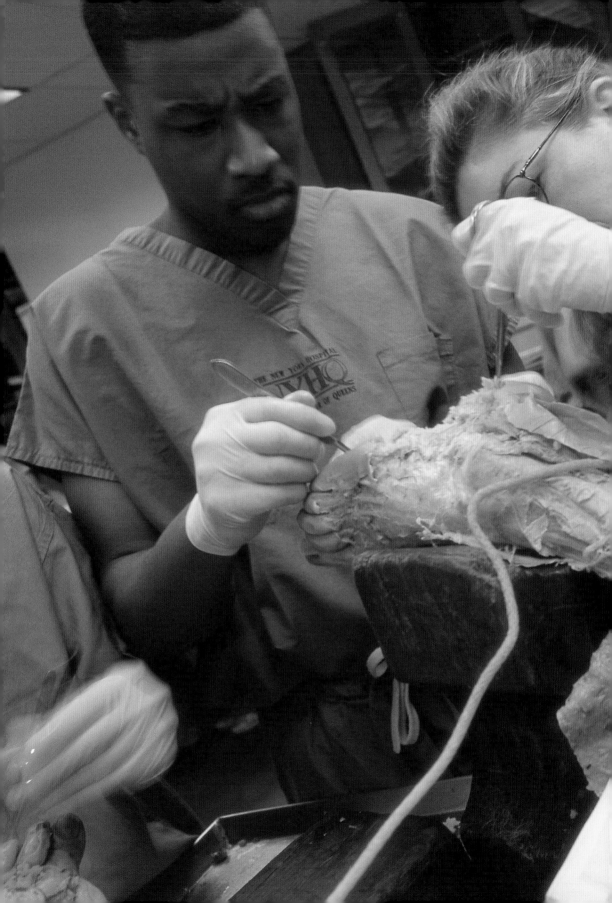

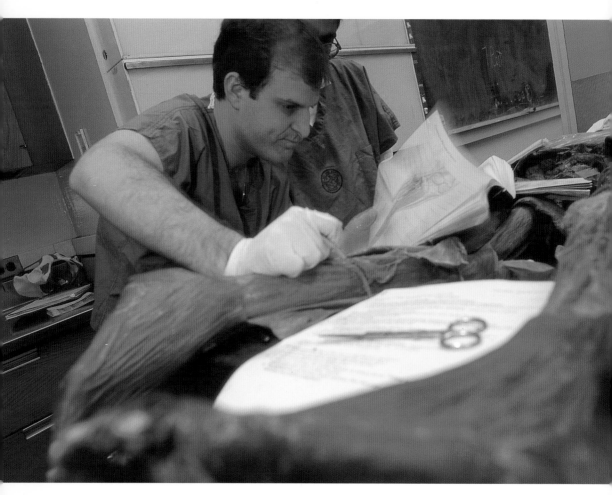

David working on the leg dissection.

Previous page: Marcus (left) dissecting the foot.

Today was our last Anatomy practical. As I was sitting at my station waiting for the moment when I could drop my paper into the grading box and relieve myself from the burden called "Gross Anatomy," I actually began to feel a little sentimental. Why wasn't I ecstatic and jumping for joy like the rest of my classmates? I felt relieved, yet somehow a little sad to be finished.

When I began this course, I was challenged to my limits. The sheer volume of material and the reality that the person on the table was actually at one point a living, breathing soul overwhelmed me. I remember feeling unsure of myself, my confidence rattled to the bone, as I spent night after night trying to figure out how to study the volumes of material given to us.

After a week or two of struggling to keep my head above water, and incessantly questioning myself, my motivations, and my abilities, I began to realize something. Despite the countless hours I was spending in the anatomy lab, despite the lingering pungent odor of the formaldehyde which remained in my nostrils long after I'd left the lab for the night, I was doing something that most people could never even dream of doing. I had forgotten how fortunate I was to have the opportunity to learn about the intricate, subtle mysteries of the human body. Selfishly, I had forgotten the sacrifice made by the individuals and their families who had selflessly offered their bodies to us for study.

As the weeks progressed and I delved into the thorax and then the abdomen and pelvis, I further understood the amazing feat of such complex parts uniting to form such a perfectly efficient machine. I began to love learning the material just for the sake of learning. Anatomy no longer felt like a burden, but rather a gift.

–David

The final practicum.

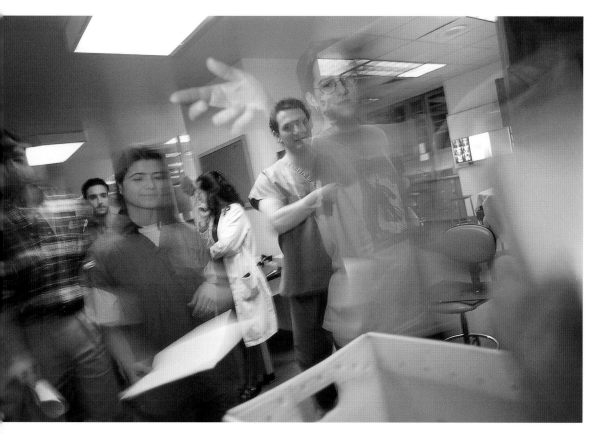

Andria (left) and Rebecca (right) handing in their final exam papers.

I think that I began planning the memorial service for Gross Anatomy before the course even started. Nestled in my general nervousness was a fear that I would not be allowed the outlets I would need to get through this. My fears were in part justified. We were immediately saddled with all sorts of work, exams, and academic responsibilities. This left me with little time to reflect on the magnitude, honor, unpleasantness, and spirituality behind what we were doing (cutting, sawing, digging, pulling) to a real, once-live human being. My group didn't even give our cadaver a name.

But, yes, I got through Anatomy—everyone did—without taking too many study breaks for reflection. The last practical took place. Spring break loomed near. And we all seemed okay with things. But I had this nagging feeling that "okay" was not enough, so I decided once and for all to give both finality and a real beginning to our Anatomy experience. I would plan a memorial service with two of my classmates.

We opted to organize the service without the participation of the hospital chaplains because we did not feel comfortable having them dictate the form of our reflections. My reflections were spiritual, another student's religious, and another's focused on gratitude and appreciation to the individuals who gave of themselves in the most physical and literal way possible.

Some people lit memorial candles. One person read a passage by Shakespeare. Another read a personal diary entry. Yet another recited an old Hindu prayer that he was taught by his family when he was a child. Some students cried. Even one of the course directors became emotional at one point, which confused me at first. Surely after teaching this course for so many years, he had become desensitized, I thought. But for him, it turns out, each year brings a new class, new bodies, and new forms of reflection.

I found it hard to become very emotional about these prosections, these bodies, these individuals, these first patients of mine. Maybe I am on my way to acquiring some of the tools I will need to become a physician—a scary thought though, because that is not the kind of physician that I would like to become. However, I felt emotionally freed after the memorial and, more importantly, I felt closure. So did many of my classmates, who thanked me for making sure that this service happened. But I wonder—must we have a memorial service each time we encounter death in some form or another? It worries me a little that we (or I) needed the service to step back for this all-important reflection, something so many of us could not or would not have done on our own, individually. Hopefully, dealing with death will be different—not easier, just different—the next time around.

–Carrie

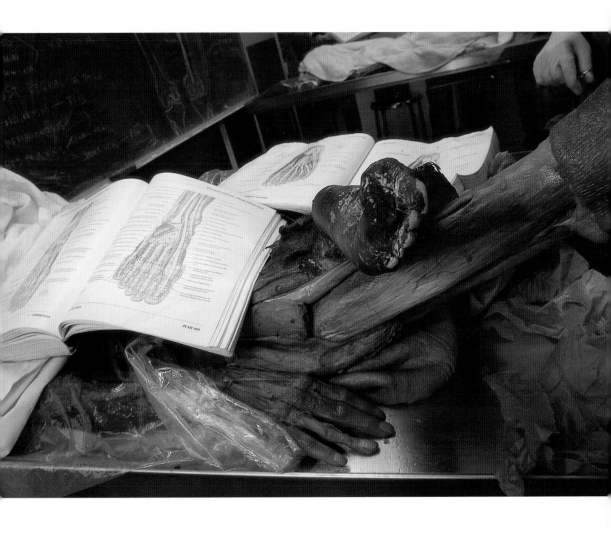

Strangely, my most emotional responses to Anatomy have been in retrospect. While reflecting on the course, I've allowed my emotional side to be involved in a way that I could not do previously. During the course, it was like a survival mechanism took over: repress all sentiment, the thing in front of you is, indeed, a thing, not a person, not even something that once was a person. But I think about the cadaver now not as a thing, not as "my cadaver," but as Alice.

We, the six people in my group always referred to her as "Alice." And we were proud of her. She was a good cadaver. She did not smell. Her organs had not decayed. And somehow I think I believed that this preservation phenomenon was attributable to Alice herself.

Slicing through her firm, pinkish-yellowish-white skin was not what pained me. No, dissection did not disturb me. Dissection never felt like a violation of Alice or her body, not even during the pelvis. The violation came when we students neglected to wrap her body adequately at the end of the day. I was horribly upset when I saw how desiccated and black her arms had become after several weeks of exposure to air. The dissection was a collaboration between Alice and me, between Alice and the six of us who had been assigned to her. By not preserving her dissected arm, torso, etc., and allowing rot and decay to set in, I felt I had failed Alice. I had not fulfilled my part of the collaboration.

The last several weeks of the course were, therefore, somewhat harder for me than the earlier weeks, because Alice was becoming more and more dried out. As each limb withered, turned brittle and black, I really felt like we were losing her. It was almost as if Alice's presence was with us only so long as we thoroughly respected her body.

A special camaraderie developed in the lab that was truly remarkable. I do miss the course now that it is over. They say Anatomy is the great leveler. Maybe that is true. We were all empty vessels trying to be filled, helping one another to saturate our brains. No one started the course well-versed in the details of anatomy. People befriended one another in front of the CT scans on the light boxes. Strange bedfellows, so to speak. Maybe part of the bond was due to the fact that we truly needed to know *everything*. I could have read the atlases and the textbooks and the handouts cover-to-cover, and I would not have been over studying.

That camaraderie is gone now. I don't feel the same kinship with my classmates that I felt during nights in the lab reviewing organs, or during afternoons in the education center studying nerves. I miss the intensity I invested in the process. I miss that special energy that pervaded the class. I took it all for granted at the time.

–Katie

ABOUT THE STUDENTS

Page numbers in bold indicate where photos of student journal writers appear.

ANDRIA CARDINALLI-STEIN was born on March 27th, 1975 in Monterey, California where she was raised. She graduated from Stanford University with a BS in Biology. Growing up, Andria lost a teenage friend to cancer, and afterwards, volunteered in hospitals and nursing homes. By age thirteen, she knew that her fascination with the workings of the human body and mind, combined with her desire to help improve the quality and duration of people's lives, would direct her toward a career in medicine. When she began medical school, Andria thought she would go into internal medicine to treat the "whole patient." Though Anatomy was initially an emotional challenge for her, she fast became intrigued by the structure of the human body. She didn't realize the degree of that interest until her surgical rotation during her third year. She is now trying to figure out how to combine the vast knowledge required in internal medicine with the technical skill needed in delicate surgeries. She is considering studying otolaryngology (ear, nose and throat), but may train in internal medicine and specialize in gastroentrerolgy. **pp. 47, 123**

TARA LAKSHMI FERNANDO was born on March 21st, 1975 in New Haven, Connecticut where she was raised. She is the daughter of two physicians, and from a young age realized the dedication involved in the practice of medicine. Tara graduated from the Massachusetts Institute of Technology with a BS in Chemical Engineering. While there, she became fascinated with Biomedical Engineering. When she began medical school, Tara says she did not have concrete goals. However, during her third-year clerkships, she discovered a love of surgery and now plans to train in general surgery or obstetrics and gynecology. After her training, Tara hopes to remain in academic medicine, which will enable her to teach and conduct research. She is eager to integrate information technology into her work. Tara hopes that her career in medicine will offer her the chance to touch people's lives, one at a time, and enable her to make significant contributions to the quality of their lives. **pp. 49, 97**

Previous page: Candles lit at the beginning of the student-organized memorial service.

RAJIV GUPTA was born in Agra, India on January 29th, 1960. He spent his early childhood in a small village in the Thar Desert. At age nine, he moved with his parents to Pilani and and later received degrees in electrical engineering and physics at the Birla Institute of Technology and Science. At age twenty-two, he traveled to the United States to earn a PhD in Computer Science at the State University of New York at Stony Brook. Before beginning medical school, Rajiv served on the faculty of the University of Southern California, and was a researcher at GE Corporate Research and Development. Rajiv says he was awed by and lured into medicine after he observed several image-guided procedures in France.Heis especially proud of a diagnosis he made in his second year of medical school: *cutaneous leishmaniasis*, the disease that almost killed him in his early childhood after he contracted it from the wild dogs he played with in the desert. He plans to specialize in interventional radiology, though he does not yet know where he and his wife and two children will settle. **p. 64**

DAVID HASS was born on August 1st, 1974 in Philadelphia where he was raised. He graduated from Cornell University with a BA in Biology. He spent the following year as a researcher in an anesthesiology laboratory examining the effects of muscle relaxants on both human and primate physiology. When David began his medical training it was with a strong interest in pediatrics. During his clerkships, he was intrigued by the intensity of the surgical O.R., fascinated by the complexity of neuroscience in psychiatry and neurology, and amazed at the experience of delivering babies. Throughout, he has valued the emotional interactions and bed-side conversations with patients, as well as the intellectually stimulating detective process of the diagnostic workup. David plans to train in internal medicine. **p. 118**

KATHERINE BETH HISERT was born on October 22nd, 1974 in Berkeley, California where she was raised. She graduated from Brown University with a BS in Biochemistry. For one year after college, Katie worked at Gould Farm, a residential treatment facility for the mentally ill in western Massachusetts. Katie is now pursuing a combined degree of MD/PhD because she is interested in both the basic science that underlies disease and treatment, as well as the ability of the doctor to help individuals. For the next several years, Katie will spend her time doing research towards her PhD thesis in the areas of microbiology and immunology. She hopes to find a way to practice both research and medicine by training in internal medicine with a sub-specialty in infectious disease. **p. 41**

HILARY HOCHBERG was born on February 5th, 1975 in Penn Valley, Pennsylvania where she was raised. She graduated from Princeton University with a degree in molecular biology and began medical school the following year. After being tempted by many of the fulfilling paths introduced during her third year of medical school, she was drawn to the unique intellectual curiosity that internal medicine fosters. Hilary looks forward to a career that offers the privilege and challenge of helping patients and their families cope with illness, and one that offers a lifetime of learning and educating. **pp. 45, 50, 101, 102, 111**

HANSOO MICHAEL KEYOUNG was born in Seoul, South Korea on November 16th, 1973 along with his twin brother Jinsoo Andrew Keyoung who attends medical school at Georgetown. When Hansoo Michael was ten years old, his family moved to Long Island, New York, where he graduated from high school. He studied at the University of Chicago and at the State University of New York at Binghamton where he received a BS in Biology. After graduation, he worked as a summer fellow in the Department of Neurosurgery at Hartford Hospital in Connecticut conducting clinical research on patients with severe brain injuries. While applying to medical school, he worked at the Brain Trauma Foundation at Cornell University. He is now pursuing the combined research and medical degree of an MD/PhD. Hansoo Michael plans to go into academic neurosurgery to help the sick, teach residents and medical students and conduct research. For now, he is devoting his time to his PhD thesis work, studying brain stem cells and brain regeneration. **pp. 33, 71, 72**

REBECCA ANNE MIKSAD was born on September 18th, 1972 in Guildford, England. She was raised in Texas, but spent three years in England. She received a joint degree BA in Economics and

On the door of the basement anatomy lab.

Women's Studies from Harvard University. Rebecca's love for the outdoors brought her to medicine when she studied Wilderness EMT and became fascinated by the medical ingenuity and creativity required in wilderness first aid and rescue. After college, she spent a year working in South Africa at a community health center in a township and at the University of Cape Town researching barriers to access to health care. Before medical school she never considered going into a surgical or procedural field. During Anatomy she says she fell in love with dissection and the exploration of the human body. She finds the body's efficiency of design and beauty of construction awe-inspiring. At the moment Rebecca is considering either a combined surgical and medical career such as obstetrics and gynecology, or training in internal medicine and specializing in gastroenterology. **p. 123**

MICHAEL STERN was born on April 27th, 1964 in Washington, DC. He was raised in Palisades, New York and moved with his family to Manhattan during high school. He graduated from Brown University where he double-majored in studio art and art history. For nine years, Michael pursued a career as an artist, painting architectural abstractions. His work was shown in New York and around the northeastern United States, and is in private and corporate collections worldwide. At age thirty, he began a post-baccalaureate premed program at Columbia University. During his application year, he worked as a clinical research coordinator working with people with AIDS suffering from CMV retinitis. Before he began medical school he thought he would be a cardiologist, but during medical school, he became increasingly drawn to the pace and breadth of emergency medicine. During his medical studies, Michael and his wife had their second child. Being a husband and father during his training has been at times challenging, but mostly joyous and uplifting. He says that it has helped to him to better understand how wonderful and fragile life is. Michael plans to continue painting. **p. 35**

MARCUS LEJON WILLIAMS was born on May 26th, 1975 in San Francisco where he was raised. He attended Saint Mary's College of California in Moraga. In his first year there, Marcus played football and soon after decided to major in health science (a field geared for physical or occupational therapy). That same year, he fell in love with physiology and decided to pursue a career in medicine, which he hopes will enable him to positively impact the lives of others. When he began his medical training, he thought he would pursue a career in primary care, either family medicine, or general pediatrics. While in medical school Marcus decided he wanted to be a specialist, rather than a generalist. As a result, he plans to train in internal medicine and specialize in gastroenterology. **p. 116**

CARRIE L. ZINAMEN was born on May 21st, 1975 in New Rochelle, New York, and raised in New City, New York. She graduated from Harvard University with a BA in Biology and History of Science. Ever since she got a Fisher Price doctor's set for her fifth birthday, Carrie was intrigued with the idea of a career in medicine. This dream was developed and realized after many hours of volunteering in a children's hospital, teaching science to elementary school-kids at the Boston Museum of Science, and helping her younger sister through her own medical problems with *celiac disease*. Carrie is planning a residency in psychiatry. Her experience in medical school reinforced what Carrie sensed early on: she needs to practice the kind of medicine that will not only encourage, but require her to know her patients as human beings, rather than simply as their diagnoses. She looks forward to soon beginning a family, and maintaining the delicate balance between her demanding and rewarding work, and the responsibilities and joy she knows family to be all about. **p. 17**

There have been many people whose generosity, wisdom, support, and home-cooking kept me on track during this long process. It all began with Matthew Albert's help in finding the wonderful group of students and educators at Cornell. Matthew's love, encouragement, all-nighters, and endless generosity of mind and spirit were key in helping this project be born. At Weill Medical College of Cornell University, I would like to thank the Office of Academic Affairs—specifically, Dr. Daniel Alonso and Debra Gillers—for facilitating my work at the College, and for recognizing the importance of the project both for their own students and for those outside of the Cornell community. Of course, I owe great thanks to Dr. John Weber, Dr. W.D. Hagamen, Dr. Elizabeth Ramirez, and Lynette Nearn, as well as to the members of the Class of 2001 and their teaching assistants, all of whom made it possible for me to access the delicate and wonderful world of their basement anatomy lab. I would like to thank Jef Capaldi and Meredith (Hogan) Birkett at *American Medical News* for finding page space and energy for this adventure. I would also like to thank Yuko Uchikawa for her care and balance in finding a design that so well suits the content within.

I am honored to include the words of Dr. Abraham Verghese in these pages. His poetry and perspective help to ground the words of the eleven student journal keepers. The voices of Hilary, Rajiv, Michael, Tara, Katie, Carrie, Marcus, Hansoo Michael, Rebecca, David, and Andria bring a rich variety to the project that enables deep exploration of this complex experience. The openness and honesty with which this special group of students so carefully wrote is beyond what I ever could have imagined when we began this journey. I cannot express enough appreciation to my collaborators for sharing themselves in these ways.

Special thanks to Alma Guillermoprieto who had early faith in the project, and helped me to find Abraham; to Brennon Jones, Nancy Berner, and Erika Goldman who shared their publishing wisdom; to Abby Heyman and the late Ethan Hoffman who first taught me about the art of book making; and to Susan Meiselas who has taken me along on many rides, and with whom I am in constant dialogue and debate. Andi Schreiber, Laura Hubber, Dolly Meieran, Michael Wolfson, Rob Fassino, Rachel Corner, Jeff Jacobson, Elaine Albert, and Judy and Stan Levin, all said from the beginning they knew this book was going to happen. Their optimism and support helped get me through all the rejections, and celebrate the achievements. And finally, for his mild manners, great patience, and *agapi*, I would like to thank Will Kanteres. He and my stalwart four-legged companions, Majic and Lefty, have given me the time and space necessary to complete this project—usually long after they would have liked to call it a night.

This book and accompanying exhibition would not have been possible without the vision of Kathleen Foley and the Board and Staff of the the Open Society Institute's Project on Death in America, whose support enabled the project to be fully realized.

And just as the students have written of being forever touched, moved, and indebted to the individuals who gave of themselves in the ultimate way, I would like to dedicate this book to all those who have donated their bodies to further medical education. I have never before witnessed a gift that is honored, respected, and consumed so completely.

Published by **THIRD RAIL PRESS, INC.**

PO Box 356 New York, NY 10276 **e**: mlevin@igc.org

© 2000 THIRD RAIL PRESS, INC.

Photographs © MERYL LEVIN
Foreword © 2000 ABRAHAM VERGHESE
Journal Texts © by individual students as noted below each text
Diagrams and sketches from study books of individual students, reproduced with permission.

p. 20 *Subclavian/Axillary/Brachial* by Katherine Hisert; p. 23 Figure from course study packet; p. 28 *Origins/Insertions* by Katherine Hisert; p. 32 Figure from course study packet; p. 38 *PAD/DAB* by Michael Stern; p. 53 *Pulmonary Arteries* by Katherine Hisert; p. 57 *The Heart* by Katherine Hisert; p. 74 *Middle Colic* by Michael Stern; p. 79 *Abdominal Branches of the Aorta* by Rebecca Anne Miksad; p. 113 *Femur* by Katherine Hisert.

Library of Congress Catalog Card Number: 00-191693

ISBN: 0-9702744-0-8

All photographs and journal texts were created during the 1998 course ANATOMY DISSECTION AND IMAGING LABORATORY at the Weill Medical College of Cornell University in New York City.

This publication and accompanying exhibition were made possible in part by a grant from the OPEN SOCIETY INSTITUTE'S PROJECT ON DEATH IN AMERICA.

Design: YUKO UCHIKAWA

Printed and bound in China by EVERBEST PRINTING CO. LTD.